The Blue Ring

(Based On The Biography Of Marie-Jeanne)

To Tanya & Patrick with my best wishes

Meilleurs vœux

Marie-Jeanne Daw

The Blue Ring

The Blue Ring

The Blue Ring

Acknowledgments

We would like to thank all of our family and friends for their support, encouragement and advice. Unfortunately it would be almost impossible to name everyone who has contributed to the making of this book without omitting someone. We want to especially thank our relatives and close friends in France and Italy for providing additional facts, and giving us their opinions and views. Many of the names have been changed to protect their privacy.

To you, our readers, we hope we have revealed a side of World War II from a viewpoint that has rarely been written about or discussed.. We also hope that this viewpoint from the French side (and a Division of the French Underground) will be enlightening and helpful to the new generation.

Marie-Jeanne and Chérie-Lynn

The Blue Ring

Dedicated to the Memory of

Jean Vella (Nini), my brother

Alan, my son

Merritt, my husband

John P. Ellbogen (Jack), a longtime friend
whose support helped me achieve my goals.

Table of Contents

Marie-Jeanne Vella's Genealogy Chart

Father's Side
Giovanni Di Vella - Grandfather
  Jean Vella (French for Giovanni)

Teresa Di Angioli/Vella - Grandmother

Children of Giovanni Dei Vella & Teresa
Aaron (later known as Gerard Vella)
Vittorio
Armando
Pietrina

Mother's Side
Bernardo Pizzio - Grandfather
  (also known as Pépé)

Catérina Pizzio - Grandmother
  (also known as Mémé Catin)

Children of Bernardo Pizzio & Catérina
Olimpia Pizzio
Honorina Pizzio
Bernard Pizzio (Pipo)
Claudino Pizzio (Lino)
Valerino Pizzio
Adalgiza Pizzio (Ziza)

*Children of Honorine (later married to Antoine Cassini, known as Anto)
Liliane (daughter)
***Emma (daughter)

**Children of Pipo (married to Yvonne)
Jean (known as Jeannot - son)
Claude (son)
René (son)

***Emma (married Henri Luque)

Children of Gerard Vella & Olimpia
Giovanni Vella (known later as Jean Vella--nickname: Nini)
Marie-Jeanne Vella (named after Jean) (married to Merritt E. Darr)

Children of Marie-Jeanne Vella-Darr and Merritt E. Darr
Alan J. Darr
Chérie L. Darr

* * * * *

America
My Adopted Country

The harbor of New York was more like I had expected, an organized con-fusion. Officials from Security, Immigration and Customs were all headed somewhere in a hurry. Passengers were everywhere, trying to locate their lug-gage, catch a porter and get through the formalities of arrival as quickly as possible. The speakers were loud and yet unclear, in the middle of this cacophony. I felt absolutely lost!

I glanced around in dismay. Far away, at the exit of the terminal, people meeting the ship were huddled behind the gates. I tried to find Merritt, who was to have met me upon my arrival, in the crowd, but it seemed useless from such a distance.

In the harbor terminal the luggage that passengers were picking up, was displayed alphabetically from A to Z along the quay. From the ceiling enor-mous signs indicating each letter of the alphabet were very much in evidence. I went to look for my suitcases under the letter V for Vella. Once I located mine, I tried to hail a porter without success. I realized this was going to be a long procedure, and with a sigh, completely distressed, I prepared myself for a long wait. And once again I scrutinized the crowd looking for Merritt.

To my surprise there he was, waving back and forth trying to get my atten-tion. A feeling of relief swept over me. The hassle didn't matter anymore. Totally oblivious to all seeing me I waved back and was calling to him aloud even thought he was too far to hear. I was startled when an uniformed gen-tleman addressed me.

"How can I help you, young lady?" questioned this custom officer with a grin on his face. I realized I must have been talking aloud, but ignoring my embarrassment, he proceeded with his task of checking my carry-on bags, brushing my larger suitcases with a marker and after a few questions he sig-naled a porter and wished me good luck.

This was August 1955. I had just arrived from Cannes, France (French Riviera) on the "Independence". The crossing of the Atlantic Ocean lasted seven days. Merritt had come in the previous day from Alva, Oklahoma in order to meet me in New York, upon my arrival.

Followed by the porter I walked briskly towards the exit and almost ran into Merritt's arms. It had been over two years since we had seen each other. We stood there in the middle of an unbelievable chaos, unaware of anyone but ourselves. It seemed unreal, just like a dream. It brought back all the post war memories. I have no idea how long we were there in this waiting area, being pushed by the crowds, but eventually we returned to reality with the help of our porter who was anxious to get us settled. Once My luggage was safely stored in Merritt's car, we were ready to go to the Times Square Hotel, where we had two rooms reserved.

My first impression of America and especially New York was this fabulous conglomeration of skyscrapers topped by a definitely pink sky. Both the temperature and the humidity were very high. No words can describe the ride from the harbor to the hotel. I was in awe and wanted to see everything. I had my window down, until a policeman stopped us and told us to keep the windows closed, lock the doors, and even have an empty pop bottle on the seat beside the driver, for self-defense, if needed. We were crossing a rough part of the city, the officer explained and since our car had an Oklahoma license plate it would attract attention, indicating we were in transit, very dangerous in his opinion. "Use caution" were his parting words. The entire incident really brought me back down to earth. As we approached the center of the city, the sea of cars was quite impressive but most amazing was the sight of policemen directing traffic on horseback. I had never seen anything like this before. I wondered about the horses, they seemed perfectly at ease. Incredible!

The Times Square Hotel was an old building located on an extremely busy street. Merritt had checked in the night before and was all settled. I was shown to my room on a top floor, where the sound of the outside traffic seemed as if it were directly in my room. From my window, people looked like ants. After checking my surroundings and getting briefly organized, I took a quick shower and changed clothes for the third time. Onboard the ship I had put on a linen suit first, once on deck as we were nearing the Statue of the Liberty, I decided my choice was wrong. I replaced it with a light summer dress I had in my carry-on bag. The phone rang several times before I recognized its sound among the loud noise reverberating around me, even with the windows permanently closed.

"Are you ready to get acquainted with your new country?" Merritt asked.

"Of course" I replied, "I'll be right down."

In no time, he was knocking at my door.

The first thing I had to do was to send a wire to my mother in France, informing her of my safe arrival. The lobby of the hotel conveniently had a Western Union desk for this purpose. I was sure that my family would worry about my crossing of the Atlantic and if I had been met as planned. Among a very enthusiastic message, I remember mentioning the "Pink Sky" because on the Riviera (called appropriately "Cote d'Azur") the sky is unbelievably blue.

"What would you like to do first? We could take a taxi and go sightseeing, or walk along Times Square, go to Fifth Avenue and do some shopping, just name it", said Merritt.

"I want to walk around, feel the people, the country, window shop. I would love to visit the Empire State Building," I replied.

We headed for the streets. The heat was unbearable. I had never felt heat like that before. Once in while, when crossing the entrance of a store, or theater, a blast of cold air would be felt and welcomed. This was my introduction to air conditioning.

As we mingled with the crowds, I was startled to hear English with a variety of accents, but what amazed me most were the little children carrying on a conversation. They sounded so grown up, so advanced.

New York was a fascinating city. We reached Fifth Avenue, went along on Broadway and cutting through some side streets we decided to stop for lunch as we came across an Italian Restaurant. The food was excellent and I had a chance to speak the language with the owner. He wanted to know how things were in Italy and in France; meanwhile, Merritt who did not understand a single word of Italian was getting impatient. With regret, knowing this was my last chance to communicate with someone from Europe, we left followed by good wishes from our effusive host.

We had so much to do and see in one day. We were leaving the next morning. Going to the Empire State Building was a must. I wanted to get a good look at the city of New York, even from at distance. We hailed a taxi and we were on our way.

We rode the speed elevator to the rooftop. That alone was a scary experience. From the top we could see and admire the entire city from all angles. It was unbelievable. Merritt, who had visited New York many times, was pointing out various areas of interest. I took pictures and was absolutely thrilled.

We started back towards the hotel, but of course we had to stop on Fifth Avenue and do some shopping. I had never seen so many shops and the display windows were a lot wider than the *vitrines* located in Paris.

On a side street a beautiful outfit caught Merritt's eye. It was a cream color silk skirt with a pattern of large flowers and various shades of green leaves, hand painted, with layers of petticoats (fashionable at the time) and a blouse of silk cream color, very chic, to match. Merritt insisted I should try it on. I protested I had a lot of clothes, beautiful clothes too as my family was in the dressmaking business, but he brushed all my arguments aside by saying: "I want to buy you something. Besides this is America."

So we went in. Of course once I tried it on I loved it. I was tall, slender, with blond hair reaching half way down my back. The saleslady took me on a platform, where I could see myself all the way around. "With your large brown eyes and your coloring, this outfit was made for you." Everyone in the store, customers and salespeople alike, were staring and smiling with approval.

Back at the hotel we tried to make reservations at Radio City Music Hall, but the show was closed that night. We decided to have dinner at the hotel and see a movie later. I returned to my room to change clothes for dinner and debated if my new outfit was not too dressy for the evening, but decided this was my only night in New York. When Merritt came to pick me up, I knew I had made the right decision.

Two years ago he had purchased a set of rings in Alva to take to France. He had stayed at this same hotel. He was scheduled to board the "Queen Elisabeth" the following day. While he was out having dinner, someone had stolen the rings, along with some other items from his locked suitcase. This time he was wearing a similar set on a chain around his neck. Before we went to dinner he pulled the chain out, removed the engagement ring, keeping the other safely on the chain. Then holding my hand, he placed the ring on my finger and with a grin he said:

"This will compliment your outfit beautifully." I was overwhelmed, speechless.

When we entered the main dining room, I knew I looked sensational. The maitre d' escorted us to a table and it seemed like we had many waiters in attendance. Ordering a meal was going to be complicated. First of all I was not familiar with the accent spoken in the area and the menu was entirely different from what I was accustomed to. I ended up ordering the same thing as Merritt, and to be honest I don't even remember what it was. After a long walk we opted for a movie theater on Broadway which was showing "Love Is A Many Splendored Thing." The theme song remained our song for the rest of our lives.

Merritt had wanted to get married right away and have a honeymoon trip back to Oklahoma, but I suggested a period of getting to know each other was a must, since we had been apart for so long. There was so much I had to learn, not only about him, but life in America as well. By the same token he did not know me either. Besides his parents were in the same country, so why not include them in our plans?

Before going to sleep that first night in a foreign country, strange room, above a noisy street, I relived the entire day since my arrival and drifted to the past two years during which I had gone through a lot of soul-searching, wondering if I was doing the right thing. Merritt had come to France a couple of times since we first met, right after World War II. The last time he had come from America, a little over two years ago to convince my family of his good intentions.

At the time the government was very reluctant to issue visas. I had to wait two years for the quota, followed by the issuance of the visa. All along my family didn't really believe that I was going to go anywhere, but when the date was set, each voiced their opinion. Did I realize I was leaving all of them, my relatives and friends, my roots and heritage behind? Would I be accepted? I could definitely find work if I was left stranded since I had worked for the Allies, but I should not forget that English was my third language and probably would not qualify me for very many jobs.

Mémé Catérina, my 85-year-old grandmother said to me,

"Go and follow your heart. You have proven that you can take care of yourself in this country. I have no doubt you will succeed. And when you do" she added, "remember to share your experience with your children, family and friends. Write a book of your incredible life story. Believe me, it will be very interesting and educational for the new generations to come. Some will learn from it, others will be touched."

I laughed, hugged her and said:

"You are just being prejudicial. Write a book? Really! In my third language, English, how ludicrous."

My only other support came from my cousin Henri. He was a bright young man. Not only had he managed to escape from a German camp, he had built a nice business in ready-to-wear clothing for men and women in Marseille. He was extremely encouraging and his opinion meant a lot to me.

Nevertheless, here I was in New York. I wanted to enjoy the moment and get reacquainted with Merritt. I wanted to be sure. Americans were known for taking marriages lightly, whereas in France, probably because most people were Catholic, divorces were a serious matter. I loved Merritt very much, but was love enough? What about him? Would he have given up all he had in his country and move to France for love? I actually had mixed emotions; most everyone at home was against my decision. Did they know something I didn't? Those seven days across the Ocean seemed such a long way away and we still had close to three full days of driving before we reached our destination. Eight days had gone by since I left home and I had to admit I was already homesick and a little apprehensive. I had to face the fact that not only would I miss my past life with all that it entailed, I had to start a new one, in a new country of which I knew close to nothing.

I must have fallen asleep in the early hours of the morning, for when the phone rang, I felt as if I had just closed my eyes. This was my wake-up call; it was time to get ready.

I met Merritt in the coffee shop for breakfast. We both ordered pancakes. I had no idea what they were and did exactly what he did; put the butter on first then syrup, and at the first bite I almost gagged. The hot cakes were salty, so was the butter and the hot syrup was sickeningly sweet. The combination of salt and sugar made me nauseated so I settled for toast.

Finally, we were on our way. I was put in charge of the map, and I followed our progress as well as the scenery. I had so many questions. I was aware that eventually I would drive people out of their minds, and in the process look extremely dumb but I had to know. I waited until we were out of the heavy traffic before I started to ask a few questions. At first I believe Merritt was flattered that he knew so much and must have felt important, but I knew that eventually he was going to get tired. As the day advanced, with windows down and the roaring sound of the traffic on the highway I concentrated on my own thoughts, and I had many.

We made several stops during the day; we had lunch in a nice little town where people were very friendly, which made our traveling enjoyable. Late that evening we stopped at a motel where we found two rooms and a restaurant nearby. We were exhausted. After a quick freshening up, I went to the dining room, where I found Merritt selecting songs on a little square box with buttons located on the wall next to the booth where he was setting.

"This is like a jukebox. You have to put in a certain amount of coins then select a song for everyone to hear. What would you like?"

I glanced at the songs, but all were unfamiliar.

"You choose, this is all new to me."

"What if a person didn't like your choice of songs, then what?" I added.

"Too bad, they would just have to bear with it I guess, I never thought about it that way," he looked puzzled.

I picked up the menu; among the specials that day was "chicken fried steak." I decided to try it. I liked chicken. However when my dinner came, I realized it was not chicken at all. It was served with a white sauce called gravy so much for that. I decided American food had much to be desired. Merritt made the remark that I had hardly touched my food, diplomatically I answered:

" I am more tired than hungry."

I went to bed immediately after dinner and fell asleep quickly.

The next day I woke up early, feeling much better. Ready to face the new day I went to the coffee shop; the place was empty. I sat at the counter and ordered coffee as I opened the breakfast menu.

"Where are you from?"

These were the first words the owner said to me. He was no doubt referring to my accent. Little did I know that I was to be haunted with this question for the rest of my life. To this day I usually reply with a smile:

"From the south," and love to see the questioning look on their faces. However, if questioned in a nice way I add: "Of France".

I ordered breakfast, being very careful not to mix sweet and salty ingredients together. He looked me over curiously and said:

"Is the menu hard for you to read?"

"Not at all," I replied. "I am just careful because in this country you do not seem to call things by their proper name."

"Such as?" he inquired.

"Well for instance the chicken fried I had last night was not chicken at all."

He laughed "Next time try the fried chicken, it is good, have you ever had it?"

"No, I assume it must be a specialty of this country" I replied.

I was baffled! Try to make sense, to a foreigner, of the difference between chicken fried and fried chicken.

Some other customers came in and that was the end of our conversation. Needless to say another obstacle I had to face was to tolerate American food. I knew exactly what I was going to do. First I was going to concentrate on one problem at a time, try to find things I could live with, the rest, I told myself, I would change.

We had driven close to four hundred miles the first day, we were somewhere in Ohio, and planned to reach Missouri on the second day, from there we would be able to reach Alva, Oklahoma, on the third day, but this was

7

pushing it. When we stopped for lunch I decided to get my hair cut shorter, about 3 inches or so, it would be cooler. From then on, the trip was enjoyable, as well as educational, but the heat was unbearable.

Merrit Darr above.   Marie-Jeanne Vella-Darr right.

It was close to midnight when we reached Alva, Oklahoma on the third day of our trip. Merritt had called his folks to tell them of our approximate arrival time and when we reached our destination, the house was all lit up and there were many cars in front. Everyone was waiting. We received a wonderful welcome. Merritt had four sisters, the youngest Rosie, still lived at home, the other three, Linda, Delza and Kay, had all come from different states with their families. I was overwhelmed and my doubts evaporated.

The next day a similar welcome took place; this time friends came to call. The Darrs were well known. They owned and operated the Alva Hotel and Coffee Shop, in the center of town. Merritt, his father Jack and his mother Cynthia took turns supervising the running of the business with some hired help.

I was written up in the local paper, had several pictures published, then received an endless amount of mail. Some welcome notes even had the newspaper's clipping attached.

Alva was a quaint little town with a population of around 8000. It was, and still is, the center of a large wheat and ranch area, as well as the home of Northwestern Oklahoma State University. I found the country absolutely beautiful. The many shades of green and yellow of the fields formed an incredible carpet, highlighted by clusters of dark green trees as far as one could see, on this flat land. Here and there some silvery streams playing hide and seek among shrubs, were very refreshing.

This was my introduction to America and the beginning of a new life for me.

.....

Following the advice of my grandmother Caterina, throughout my life I kept records of all the events that occurred while growing up in Europe. But somehow it was painful for me to even mention them. Later as I suffered some agonizing tragedies, going back to those days became a protective blanket against my grief. I realized I had to put this story together for the benefit of my remaining child, my daughter *Cherie*. I wanted her to know her heritage and be proud of it. I also wanted her to realize how lucky she was to be an American, and to appreciate the good and the bad. I hope I have guided her in the right direction. I mainly want her to uphold our family beliefs.

Mémé Catérina would be very proud. *Cherie* and I are both writing this book. As she follows my life I hope it helps her to put her own life in perspective. I also hope this book will be of help to the new generations.

Here is my story.

**Cynthia, Rosie, Jack and Delza.
Merritt's parents and sisters.**

Delza, Linda, Marie-Jeanne, Rosie and Kay.

The entire Darr family.

Our Family Roots

Our Family Roots

Somehow I can't help thinking of all the times when my brother Nini and I would sit listening to grandfather Jean recount all the events that brought him and grandmother from the *Islands of Malta* to the border town of *Menton* on the *French Riviera*. Sometimes during these narratives, I felt like he was just reminiscing aloud, forgetting that we were even in the room listening to him. Nini and I were so fascinated with his story about our ancestors that we continued to be mesmerized even though we were being ignored as he described our family's past history.

I can remember grandfather Jean's story beginning something like this:

The *Maltese Islands* are located in the *Mediterranean*, south of *Sicily* which included the islands of *Malta, Gozo and Comino*. The city of *La Valletta* was the capital of the islands. The French under Napoleon Bonaparte took *Malta* from the Knights of Saint John in 1798. British forces drove out the French in 1800. The people of Malta offered control of the colony to Great Britain. Britain's control was not completely recognized, however, until peace was made with France in 1815, after the Napoleonic Wars. Great Britain developed its Mediterranean military headquarters on *Malta*. During World War I (1914-1918), *Malta* served as a strategic naval base for the Allied forces. Great Britain granted *Malta* a measure of self-government in 1921. However, political crises in *Malta* caused Britain to revoke this *Maltese* political power. Malta's constitution was suspended in 1930 because of a dispute between the state and Roman Catholic authorities. The constitution was re-established in 1932, then withdrawn a year later. This time the pro-Italian sympathies of the Maltese government led Britain to suspend the constitution. Full authority was returned to the governor in 1936.

During World War II (1939-1945), *Malta* controlled the vital sea lanes between Italy and Africa. The natural rocks and deep inlets of the colony concealed anchorages and submarine bases. Many underground passages provided bomb shelters. Fighter planes based on *Malta* defended convoys of ships.

A constitution approved in 1962 provided that the colony become a state with internal self-government. Britain agreed to grant full independence in May 1964. But disagreement among *Malta's* political factions delayed the action until September 1964.

Baron Giovanni Di Vella lived on the island of *Malta* near the capital city *La Valletta*. He was a well respected magistrate (a judge) with a large family. Though very strict, he also had a kind and understanding side. His eldest son, named after himself, "Giovanni Di Vella", was the next in line to inherit the family title.

Giovanni Di Vella's family were good friends with Marchese Guiseppe Di

Angioli's family and used to get together and socialize quite frequently. Guiseppe was the City's District Attorney. He was a "straight-laced" gentleman and had numerous children of whom his daughter Teresa was his youngest and his favorite.

Young Giovanni, hopelessly attracted to Teresa, eventually professed his love to her. As their love for one another grew, they approached their parents with their wish to get married. Giovanni was 18 and Teresa was not quite 17. The parents of both advised them to wait until they were older. However, Giovanni persistently continued to ask permission to court Teresa. The answer was always "No" and he was given all sorts of excuses. Nonetheless, it seems that neither family thought their union would bring a lasting marriage.

They were both very different. As a teenager, young Giovanni did well in school, had high ideals, but felt constricted. No one knew why, not even himself. This could have been because of his upbringing, having to live up to his family's strict expectations, being reminded that as the eldest son he had to be an example for his brothers and sisters, to prove himself, or perhaps simply because he had lived on a small island since birth and needed open spaces and adventures.

On the other hand, Teresa was shy, quiet, and had been brought up an accomplished lady. She had always led a cosseted life with servants answering her smallest wishes and desires. She spent a lot of time just worrying about what to wear to various functions. She attended school and tea parties, did needlepoint, and charity work.

The "Di" in both families' last names indicated that they were "Blue Blood" or titled. Young Giovanni, being the eldest son would inherit the title. However, Teresa would not inherit hers. Titles were always handed down to the eldest son first. If anything should happen to him, it would be passed on to the next son in line, and so on and so on. In the case where there were no sons, it would be passed on to the eldest daughter. The difference, however, was that it would end with the daughter. It could not be passed on to her children as it could for a son. She would assume her husband's name and he may or may not have a title. Titles were very important in those days. The dynasty of her name would end with her, but her children could still be considered "Blue Blood" which was a way to show their "upper class" stature in society.

Having done the best they could to convince their parents, Giovanni and Teresa finally decided to run away together against their parents' will. In the 1800s, people of breed were not allowed to fall in love and refuse to obey their parents. This was particularly serious because they were both minors. Marriages were prearranged between one family and the other taking in consideration their standing in society, their title, fortune and wealth, mainly because these had been passed down century to century, from their ancestors and all rules about one family joining another applied.

It was very difficult to earn a title if you did not inherit it. Only on very rare occasions titles could be earned by performing some outstanding duty for their country or their king.

Most of these families were very large and needed a lot of money, much more than they had, so prearranged marriages were helpful in keeping the costs down.

Grandfather often dreamily would recount the excitement to be free, to be together, and to run as far away from *Malta* as they could. Neither were prepared for the hardships they were to encounter. After a while, they ran out of money. The "fantasy life" was replaced by the hard reality of having to do things including the everyday chores and fending for themselves. This was a life style they never knew and they later admitted that they had been too hasty and should have waited a little longer, be more prepared. It was, however, too late.

When Giovanni and Teresa ran away, they disgraced not only themselves, but both families as well. Naturally, their parents were crushed. In order to "save face," the families had to act as if neither their children nor their marriage ever existed. (They had married on board ship after lying about their age). Giovanni Di Vella Senior made arrangements so that the title would go to the next son in line. Since Giovanni was a judge this demanded exemplary conduct not only for himself, but his family as well. How could anyone in office be fair and decide the right or wrong of others when he could not even control this in his own family, especially his son?

Meanwhile, Giovanni and Teresa headed for the *Balkans*. Wanting to avoid being caught by their respective families, they boarded the first ship out of *Malta* which was destined to go to *Turkey*. They surprisingly succeeded in convincing the captain to marry them on board. Then, the couple traveled through *Montenegro*, where Giovanni, not being able to find work, enlisted in the military which was under the French command. Giovanni never told us where Teresa was while he was in battles, nor did he give us many details concerning the battles themselves. He did, however, receive many citations and medals for his accomplishments and even showed them to us with a great amount of pride.

The *Balkans* are a group of countries that cover a peninsula in the southeast corner of Europe. The countries are named after the *Balkan* mountains in *Bulgaria* and *Yugoslavia*. The word *Balkan* is the word for mountain in the Turkish language. The area had been called "The Powder Keg of Europe" because so many wars had begun there. It also seems that other countries, such as France, England, Germany, and Russia would join in the battle, either to help restore the peace or sometimes to create more confusion. No one really knows.

The Serbo-Bulgarian War (November 13, 1885 – March 3, 1886) was no different. This conflict demonstrated certain inadequacies of the Balkan peace settlement fashioned by the Congress of Berlin, 1878.

The settlement was upset when a coup d'etat occurred in *Eastern Rumelia* (September 18, 1885) and that autonomous province of *Ottoman Turkey*, announced its unification with *Bulgaria*. *Serbia*, which had been dissatisfied with the extent of the territory allotted to it by the Treaty *of Berlin*, was opposed to the strengthening of its rival, *Bulgaria*. After the coup d'etat, the *Serbian* Prince Milan, who also hoped that an aggressive foreign policy would relieve his domestic problems, demanded that *Bulgaria* cede some of its territory to *Serbia*. An international conference was convened to consider how the powers should respond to *Bulgaria's* enlargement and to *Serbia's* claims. It became deadlocked in November of 1885 and *Serbia* declared war. Prince Milan accepted an armistice only when *Austria-Hungary* threatened to enter the war in *Serbia's* defense. The Treaty of *Bucharest* (March 3, 1886) which concluded the war, reestablished the prewar *Serbo-Bulgarian* borders and left *Bulgaria* and *Eastern Rumelia* united.

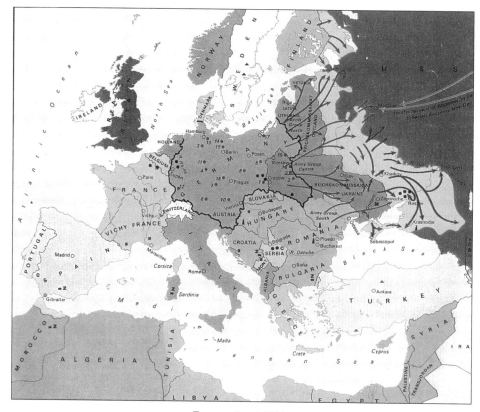

Europe about 1941.

When my grandfather, Giovanni was discharged, he petitioned to relocate to *Menton*, on the *French Riviera*. He also changed his name upon becoming a French citizen. Giovanni was changed to the French translation which is "Jean" and Di Vella became "Vella." They quickly settled in as a family and had three sons and a daughter. The boys were Aaron (named after the King of Egypt), Vittorio (named after the King of Italy), and Armando. The girl was named Pietrina.

Our Family Roots

When Aaron started school, he began to use his middle name, Gerard, to avoid being teased. Being tall and slender with large dark brown eyes, he was quite handsome. Moreover, his wit, charm and ambition often worked in his favor. However, he was also known to be unpredictable, unreliable at times, and quite a playboy. Being a promotional sales representative, he frequently took business trips to the *Italian Riviera*. On one of his trips, he met Olimpia.

At a distance of only 15 kilometers from the coast, *Perinaldo* is situated on the top of a small mountain and offers a wonderful view both over the sea and over the Alps. *Perinaldo*, founded in the XI century by Count Rinaldo di *Ventimiglia*, was a holiday resort with hotels, restaurants and good inns. The road which links this pretty village with the *Via Aurelia*, near Vallecrosia, winds amongst flower-fields and olive groves and the trip can be made in about twenty minutes.

Napoleon the First in 1797, during his campaign in Italy, stopped there. It is the native place of the well-known astronomers: Giandomenico Cassini (1625-1712) and Giacomo Filippo Maraldi. Cassini's castle with its tower from where he studied the vault of heaven, and a church he ordered to be built on the Ligurian meridian, are still there. In the parish church, dedicated to St. Nicolo and recently restored, there is a valuable artistic painting: "La Madonna del Suffragio" (Our Lady of Support) whose painter is unknown.

It is possible to make beautiful excursions to: *Monte Bignone*, *Monte Caggio*, *Monte Ceppo*, *San Romolo* and to the neighboring villages, easily reached by panoramic asphalt roads, which run amongst Pine and Chestnut-woods. *Perinaldo's* inhabitants are principally floriculturists (roses and mimosas) and agriculturists (wine and olive oil). Thanks to its splendid position in the hill country, distant from the sea as from the more elevated mountains, *Perinaldo* has a very mild climate and is an ideal place for a holiday.

Perinaldo located in the Alps (Italian Riveria) above San Remo and Ventimiglia

The Blue Ring

Bernardo Pizzio, a lawyer by trade, had been elected to the office of Mayor of *Perinaldo*. He was also the conductor of the Municipal Band. Bernardo played five different instruments and was very fluent in Latin and French besides his native language, Italian. His wife, Caterina owned the only store in town and one would have to buy everything he needed at her market. Otherwise, the next market was in *Ventimiglia*.

The Pizzio's had three boys and three girls. The boys were named Bernard, nicknamed Pipo (to avoid confusing him with his father), Claudino, nicknamed Lino and Valerino. The girls were Olimpia, Honorine, and Zize (Adalgisa). They had a large home which the family had built in 1892. It had three levels with balconies built all around. The home was located next to the Maraldi Castle.

On the ground floor, there was a large kitchen and a very spacious dining room with large doors opening into a yet larger room known as "La Salla". This room was where the Municipal Band would come to rehearse and where many large parties and gatherings were held. The other two floors were small apartments that had bedrooms with sitting rooms and mini kitchens. There were a total of six apartments. Bernardo had designed this house so that all of his children would continue to come and be together, having a place to stay during the summer. He thought that as his children grew up and had their own families to raise, they would continue to come and stay, having their own privacy. They would, however, be able to get together with the other children and their families for meals in the main dining room on the ground floor. To this day, his idea worked and every summer, the families get together and stay in this home following this long-time tradition.

The Pizzio's were very much liked and respected in the community. They helped others constantly with free food and medications from their store and often Bernardo would even give them free legal advice for their personal affairs. Once a week, the Municipal Band would come and rehearse at Bernardo's home. The Band was composed of about fifteen to twenty musicians. On

A street in Perinaldo.

16

Views from our balcony.

rehearsal night, however, there were always more than forty people gathered which made the rehearsals more like social gatherings. They would serve wine and various desserts as the band would conduct its rehearsal. All this was during the era prior to Mussolini and his Fascist Party.

Then, in 1922, the Fascist Party came into power, marking the end of a happy life for the Pizzios. Bernardo was thrown in jail for refusing to join the Fascist Party. They submitted him to what they called the "purge". He was forced to drink castor oil, and they severely tortured him. After several days of this, they released him but he never recovered. Feeling disgraced, hurt and resentful, he literally worried and starved himself to death. He finally died at the young age of 52, leaving behind a very bitter widow. This was truly a devastating time for Caterina. The Fascists had not only taken the life of her husband, but they even took away her livelihood, her general store. It provided the only income besides the cultivation of her family's lands.

Catérina loathed Mussolini and all that were connected with the Fascist Party and their beliefs. In the family's opinion, the Fascists had killed Bernardo and revenge was the only thing that could quell Caterina's bitterness. As the children grew up, they left *Perinaldo* to live a better life in France, away from tyrants and politics.

Only Olimpia, the oldest daughter and Valerino, the youngest son remained. Being an excellent seamstress, Olimpia did sewing for several affluent ladies in the community. Valerino, took care of the lands that the family owned, cultivating the crops and protecting their property. He also was the handyman around the house.

Olimpia was petite and slender, giving her a somewhat fragile appearance. This, however, was contradictory to her personality. She was very confident, determined, strong-minded and often did not hesitate to show her scorn for the Fascists who were all around them. She had sandy-blonde hair, big brown eyes, a pretty smile and an extremely beautiful figure. She loved to dance, to sing and was the winner of several beauty contests.

When her father was living, he would often hold large parties at his home, selecting members from his band to play. Since Olimpia was extremely young at the time, he did not allow her to come where the dance was held. The band would set up in a corner of the Pizzio's large ballroom. Wanting to be part of it all, but undetectable, Olimpia would get all dressed up, in an effort to look much older. She would then sneak down from her room and get lost in the crowd. Instructing her partners to stay at a certain distance away from her father, she would dance all night. Bernardo, extremely near-sighted would have no idea she was ever there. This went on for years with no one ever telling him. Olimpia often wondered if he might have finally known but pretended not to.

Since Olimpia was extremely attractive and talented, her family encouraged her to enter the local beauty contests. She was the winner on many of them. At one of these contests held in the city of *San Remo*, she met Gerard Vella. Olimpia was extremely set in her ways and at that time, marriage was not a priority. She had helped her mother raise five brothers and sisters, and for now, that was enough. Gerard made many trips to *Perinaldo* to convince her otherwise. She eventually gave in to his proposals and they married several months later.

To Olimpia's dismay, their marriage never fulfilled her expectations. Even though married, Gerard remained a bachelor at heart and was reluctant to give up his playboy ways. In desperation, Olimpia tried to save their rocky marriage by convincing Gerard that they should settle down and have a family. She became pregnant the following summer. When their son was born, they named him Jean (named after grandfather Vella). He later, however, preferred the nickname, Nini (which is derived from Giovanni), and used that the rest of his life.

Unfortunately, this birth caused even more difficulties between them. Gerard's lack of commitment to save their marriage led to a lengthy separation. Three years later, they reunited and had a little girl whom they named Marie-Jeanne. They now lived in *Juan-les-Pins*, *au Pont du Lys*, near *Antibes*. This was and still is a very popular beach tourist resort in the heart of the *French Riviera* (the Côte d'Azur). Gerard being forever a free spirit caused the marriage to end, with both of them going their separate ways.

Juan les Pins

This is where I was born. Juan les Pins-Antibes was then one town.

The First Years Of My Life

I do not remember much at that stage in my life except seeing myself as a little girl lying on a table under bright lights in a strange room. People draped in white with only their eyes exposed as though specters bent over me.

The way it was explained to me later, it all started with my mother's custody battle over her children. She had by then become an accomplished seamstress and was earning a good living. However, the pressures of her ongoing separation from Gerard plus working full time and raising two children caused numerous difficulties.

After a very bitter altercation with my father, grandmother Teresa, who loved my mother dearly, offered to keep Nini, while she would help her run away with me, since I was still a baby. My mother agreed, but it never came to pass.

At that time, it was customary to nurse children by breast-feeding them. With all the stresses affecting my mother's health, she did not get the proper nutrients and her diet was severely lacking the essential vitamins including calcium and iron. With the natal care not as advanced as today, mothers were not checked on a regular basis. Therefore, she did not realize that I was being extremely undernourished.

When I was 18-months-old, I fell down from a highchair and I injured my left hip. This injury became further aggravated due to my malnutrition as a baby (my bones were very brittle according to the medical sources) causing further complications. I was then taken to "La Clinique Lanval" in *Nice, France* and remained there for almost one year and a half. The doctors had told my parents that if I survived, there would be a possibility that I would be crippled. The next few months would be crucial in determining the extent of my recovery. I required lots of therapy and needed to replace my cast every three months which covered my entire left leg and a portion of my torso.

There was no way my family could cover the expenses. Fortunately my long stay was paid by a philanthropic organization financed and sponsored by movie stars. This organization, consisting of mainly American celebrities, supported the children's clinic by giving personal donations and holding various fund raisers. The biggest fund raiser which they held once a year in *Nice, France* was known as "Le Bal des Petits Lits Blancs", ("The Ball of the Little White Beds"). The "crème de la crème" would attend this magnificent event in the heart of the French Riviera. Without their financial help, I would not be who and where I am today. Even now, I still enjoy being around celebrities and working for them as an interpreter. I never accepted money for my services since I felt this was the least I could do. A way of showing my gratitude for what they had done for me as a child.

The Blue Ring

I was finally released from "La Clinique Lanval" at the age of 3. The doctors recommended that to speed my recovery, the mountain air would be beneficial. Therefore my mother thought that her native home in *Perinaldo, Italy* would be the best place for my recuperation. She was no longer living with my father and felt I would also be relatively safe from him. My mother always feared that he might take me away, not out of fondness for me, but as a means of getting even with her. Having the Italian border between my father and I made my mother feel much safer.

There were already three family members living with "Mémé" Catérina. ("Mémé" is an affectionate way to say Granny). They were my aunt Honorina, a widow and her daughters Liliane and Emma. Liliane was 7 years old and Emma was 5. Both my aunt and my mother had to go out of town to work in the surrounding larger cities. Unfortunately, *Perinaldo* was too small of a town to supply any well-paying jobs.

My mother, from her balcony with Mémé.

When the mothers were away, Mémé Caterina was in charge and watched us three girls. Although she was strict, she wanted us to make important decisions and would give us a certain amount of freedom so that we would learn to be independent and think for ourselves. At first, I was frequently ill and had difficulty walking but the tranquil mountain air helped immensely. Occasionally, when I felt discouraged at my slow progress, Mémé Catérina, who would not allow self-pity, always made "light" of even the most painful moments. These priceless memories became a major influence of how I approach and see life today.

We all had wonderful memories of growing up in *Perinaldo*. Money was scarce, but in spite of this, our family was very happy. Tante Honorina and my mother would come home whenever they could. My mother was a governess for a very wealthy family. Her job consisted of mainly supervising the servants. She had first started out as a seamstress and then was promoted to governess of the household. Olimpia was treated just like family and as soon as her employers realized how much my mother worried about me, they insisted that she bring me along with her. Since the family already had three children who stayed in the nursery where they were supervised all day, one more wouldn't make any difference. However, Olimpia wisely declined. Due to the fact that my mother was an employee of this family, she felt that it would be a conflict of interests. She realized that I would be an outsider and perhaps treated differently by the other children and that the servants who worked for her would be resentful. The best solution for me was to remain with her mother in Italy.

Marie-Jeanne

Mémé Catérina owned and maintained various fields in the area.

Perinaldo, located in the Alps, was perched at the top of a mountain surrounded by valleys and numerous hills. These hills were landscaped in terraces. Mémé owned several terraces of land, some were strictly reserved for carefully spaced olives trees, others for vineyards. In the lower part of the valleys, near a water stream, she grew fruits and vegetables. She also kept a garden next to our house, where the most needed produce was available for our own personal use; on the terrace below there were cherries and apples trees.

But her favorite land was located at the end of the village. There she owned three terraces reserved to floriculture. The first one was entirely covered with roses, the second one had carnations, and the third one had incredible Mimosa trees. The land not only was the best in her opinion, it was also conveniently located at a short distance from her home, where she would be able to keep an eye on it at all times. These flowers she sold to a perfume factory located in Grasse, France, which was considered the capital of the perfume industry, on the Riviera.

Once a year the olives were gathered and locally processed into Olive Oil. In the same way, after the "*vendanges*", the grapes were taken to a nearby town and turned into excellent wine. Her products were marketed not only in Perinaldo but in the neighboring towns as well, and *Mémé* made a good living.

When Mémé went to work her fields, leaving the three of us alone, she would give us all kind of instructions: our doors were to remain locked. If a stranger rang our door bell, we were to tell whoever it was to return later, but only from the upstairs window, or we had the choice not to respond at all, pretending as if no one was home.

She would address me in particular as if I were the most reliable in these circumstances, but also I suspected, in order to restore my confidence. She was aware that I needed to regain my self-esteem and not to feel like an invalid.

Liliane and Emma were actually relieved, when I was assigned some duties by Mémé Caterina. At times, they acted as if they were frightened of various noises within the house and followed me around a lot, but in general they were very helpful and I could not help wondering if they did so, per Mémé's instructions, to allow me to be more sure of myself.

Liliane, Emma and Marie-Jeanne.

When someone did come to our door, the exchange of conversation was always done from the third floor window. Since this was far enough away, we would have the courage to face the outsider. Liliane and Emma would always stay in the background and let me do all of the talking.

This very large house that we were living in had been built by my grandfather in 1892. Since marble was plentiful and cheaply acquired in *Italy*, my grandfather utilized large quantities of it in building the house. Mainly made of marble and stone, this house, with its large balconies and winding staircases had seventeen rooms. At this time not everyone had the luxury of electricity, so I would have to walk up three flights of stairs with a candle to go to bed, my two cousins always trailing close behind me. The candlelight caused our shadows to reflect along the staircase, always scaring my two cousins. Windows lined one side of the staircase with large spaces between them. In the dark, different statues and antiques that were placed on the sills would often be mistaken for people by us three frightened girls. If help was needed, you could never rely on Liliane! She was always too terrified to do anything but moan. I could, however, always count on Emma. Even though she and I were petrified, if I acted tough and pretended not to care, she would not panic and would follow behind trying to be brave. I'm sure if anyone could see the three of us during these scary occasions that we ran into, they would truly have thought we were the three little stooges that had lost their minds.

If one looked through the windows, the "Castello Di Maraldi" could be seen. This large castle was the home of the famous astronomer Cassini. Having a unique opening in its ceiling, it would allow an unobstructed view, making it easy for him to study the night's skies and galaxies. My two cousins always thought they could see ghosts on top of the castle's towers and in the gardens surrounding it. When the moon was full, the castle was truly a ghastly sight. My room was near my cousins' rooms, but quite often I would have everyone sleeping in my bed. This all depended on how loud the noises in the house were or how bad the weather was. Winter in the Alps was always dreadful. In spite of my courage, I feared thunder and lightning. I would jump into bed, covering my head with the blanket to hide, not necessarily my bed either.

Mémé Catérina always made sure that we had regular balanced meals. Whenever she had to be away for the day she would always prepare lunch in advance. She finally decided it was high time to teach all of us how to prepare cold lunches; we had to learn to fend for ourselves. This was very easy. Preparing warm lunches was altogether another story. Eventually she decided to teach the two older girls how to do it, at first under Mémé's supervision, then finally by themselves.

I can remember one time when the menu planned was *pâte au beurre et fromage* (pasta with butter and cheese). It was easy enough to make, yet we didn't know how much pasta to use, so we cooked the entire package. Choosing a pot that was too small to hold all of these noodles, we stepped back in amazement at the disastrous sight. As the spaghetti cooked, the pasta grew and all of the water began to evaporate. We even added water as it cooked, to keep it from burning.

We ended up with enough pasta to feed the whole family and one big messy kitchen. When the three of us told Mémé Catérina of the incident, she laughed so hard, that tears came to her eyes. Later we received a lecture, on how we could have caused a fire and were lucky not to get hurt. Grandmother said a small prayer of thanks.

Perinaldo was always extremely cold in the winter. My mother always made sure to dress me warmly since I had been so sick. Before she would go away to work, she would stress to Mémé Catérina to be sure that I always had enough clothes on. Once a week we had a "big bath day". Mémé Catérina

The Blue Ring

Castello di Maraldi, left. On the left our home, middle. Just below our garden, bottom.

would light the kitchen stove and turn it up real high. Then she would put me close to the stove to stay warm. She would count the garments as she took them off. Once done, Mémé Catérina would wrap a heavy blanket around me while waiting for the water to warm up. Going upstairs to my bedroom, she would try to get the same amount and thickness of clothes as I had on before. The clothes normally consisted of a chemise with sleeves, one or two light t-shirts (depending on the weather), underpants, socks, a slip, a skirt, a pull-over, etc. After collecting the necessary garments, she would come down the stairs, mumbling and complaining to herself about the clothes she had chosen. Often not happy with her selection, she would retrace her steps back up the stairs, bringing more clothes in the process. Back in the kitchen it would finally be bath time or back in the blanket, depending on whether or not my grandmother was satisfied with her choice and the amount of garments. Definitely an all day event.

Our next door neighbor was a man named Ricardo who was a friend of my uncle, Valerino. They played music together and both our families were mutual friends. Pie, short for his real name Pietro, was the father and a dear friend of my grandmother. He was aware of the Pizzio's weekly bath ritual and always timed his visit at just about the end of our family's ordeal.

Pié would just holler "Catin," her nickname, as he entered the kitchen. He would look at the pile of clothes on the floor and the pile before Catin. She would talk to herself muttering, "This one's too thin I better put on two, that one's too heavy, etc." Pié would start laughing and would tell her, "Catin, I tell you this girl won't be able to move with all of these clothes on." Catin would give him a nasty look and snap back, "Mind your own business!" Nonchalantly, he would add, "Well one good thing comes of this. If she should ever meet a wolf, by the time he ate through all her clothes he wouldn't be hungry anymore." That remark made quite an impression with me.

As I grew up, I became healthier and stronger. I continued to be quite content living in *Perinaldo* and was always the happiest when my mother was home. Returning from work, my mother Olimpia would surprise me by bringing all kinds of gifts, clothes, candies but most of all lots of love.

In front of the house, on the lower level, was a movie theater. The houses and the buildings were built on the side of the mountain, with the flat roof of the theater reaching the lowest balcony of our home giving us a wonderful view of the Alps Mountains.

On top of their roof, they had several loud speakers announcing the entertainment to come and playing all kinds of music. In the summer, with all of the windows open, we could hear the music playing loudly through the entire house. I learned all of the romantic Italian songs: "Torna a Sorriento," "O Sole Mio," "Vieni Sul Mar," etc. as well as the operas; "I Pagliacci," "La Donna Immobile," "La Bohême," "Madame Butterfly," and many others. I would sing along at the top of my lungs.

When my mother stayed in *Perinaldo* on a short vacation she would sleep with me on the third floor. Waiting until I was asleep, she would sometimes sneak out and go downstairs to the "Cinema". Mémé Catérina's room was on the second floor and being a light sleeper, she could hear what was going on throughout the house, especially with us girls upstairs. When Olimpia and Honorine were in town, however, she would let her guard down a bit since she knew that they were watching their daughters and would usually be up later in the evening.

I would sometimes wake-up and find my mother gone. Guessing that she had gone to the Cinema, I would get up in the dark and trying not to make any noise, I would walk down to the theater dressed in my long, white night-gown, sometimes with slippers but often barefoot. Seeing my shoulder length blonde hair and large dark brown eyes along with my attire gave me the appearance of a little ghost.

The entrance of the theater was just under the screen. It never failed when I, the little ghost, would come and stand at the entrance everyone's attention would be distracted. The entire theater would burst out in laughter. Knowing immediately what was happening, Olimpia would become extremely embarrassed. I had done it once again! Olimpia would grab me and take me home which was not what I intended. I thought that if I came to see my mom at the theater, I would perhaps be able to stay. Of course, this never happened.

Mother and I spent many wonderful times together. Italy, almost entirely Catholic, had many churches all over the countryside named after a Saint. When a Saint's holiday occurred, the townspeople would go to that particular Saint's church or chapel to celebrate.

Each festivity would begin with a short Latin service followed by a procession, carrying the statue of the Saint being honored that day. The statue would be laden with jewelry (mostly gold chains, stones and diamonds) and offerings of all kinds from the town's population. A robed singing choir would lead the procession accompanied by the town's band and the parishioners. This parade would go through the city to the Saint's chapel or church. Arriving, they would enter with the statue and place it in the center of the church. At its place of honor, another short service would take place followed by a large outdoor party.

This affair was usually held in a park where the whole congregation could be accommodated. There would be food, drinks, singing and other activities all afternoon. Throughout the "festa", the chapel would remain open for those who wanted to pray on their own. The Catholic tradition of lighting candles at the altar was also offered to honor the celebrated Saint or in memory of the suffering or departed.

In the evening, they would construct a dance floor surrounded by "lampions" (Chinese lanterns) and hold a dance for the younger adults. The older crowd and the children would build a large campfire and there would be much singing. My mother took me to many of these events where we would sing or play guitar. In Italy everyone was very musically inclined and my family was no exception. Every member of my family either sang or played some sort of instrument. Fond memories of these frequent celebrations are still very precious to me.

"One of the celebrations of Santa Givsta"

One time in particular, I recall the celebration of St. Antoine that is held (according to the the church holiday calendar) every year on June 13 and is one of the biggest "festa". St. Antoine is the patron Saint for those who have lost something and he helps them to find it.

On the outskirts of the little town is a chapel and a large building called the "Convento". A former convent a long time ago, it now is used for celebrating St. Antoine's holiday. Next to it there is an impressive area used as a park and also a 'point of interest' with benches where older people would sit to admire the Alps in the background. This was the perfect place where large gatherings could be accommodated. Many festivities including the St. Antoine "festa" were held there.

On this day the procession goes from the main church to the chapel St. Antoine, a sign that the festivities had commenced. Laughter filled the air along with tolling bells and the sound of people greeting each other. Unfortunately, today these spirit-lifting festivities are not traditionally carried on as much as they were then.

Another fond memory of mine was a Saint's holiday celebrated in a little town called *Dolceacqua* (sweet water), located on the same mountain as *Perinaldo*. Being a few meters above sea level and near *Ventimiglia*, *Dolceaqua* is located on the bottom side of the mountain. This very strange-looking village had numerous arcades and many small walkways where people and an occasional donkey would traverse.

My mother and I went to the celebration in *Dolceaqua* and we had the time of our lives participating in all of the festivity's events. Eating ice cream, we leisurely strolled by booths of arts and crafts that were being sold. At one booth my mother purchased a little black doll wearing a grass skirt and big, dangling earrings for me. I was simply in heaven! A little black doll was something I had always wanted.

When my mother went out of town to go to work, I was once again under my grandmother's supervision. My cousins, older now, had started attending school. However I was still too young, so I would spend my days going with Mémé Catérina to tend her fields. This was always a great thrill for me. My grandmother would place a saddle on her donkey named "Nina". Baskets made of solid wood were tied to each side of the saddle where she would put her tools, lunch and other belongings. When I came along, however, Mémé Catérina would put all of her baskets of supplies on one side and place me on the other side. Enjoying the ride and taking in the view, I thought that this was a pure luxury. Mémé Catérina would walk behind the donkey giving orders. The donkey acted almost human, moving its ears or letting out a big, moaning sound, letting us know of her disapproval.

When I did not accompany Mémé Catérina, my grandmother would ride the donkey herself. From the house I could often see Mémé Catérina sitting on the donkey who refused to budge. She would have to dismount, pet her and then lead her home. Although the donkey had a mind of its own, it was considered a part of the family and no one dared to say anything against it. "Nina" was with us for 35 years, until later the Germans came and took her away. This was a big loss for our family especially my mother who had raised this donkey and had become very attached to it.

Eventually I became old enough to begin school. The Scuola Municipale di *Perinaldo* was conveniently located around the corner in front of the theater. To my surprise, I found that I was known to be very bright and everyone liked me, particularly the boys. At this time I didn't especially like boys. Therefore in order to keep the boys away, I decided to start a rumor that I wanted to become a nun when I grew up. This immediately stopped their interest. When this news got back to my grandmother, she would laugh hysterically and give me a hard time. This only encouraged me to spread the rumor further.

Being intelligent and a quick study, I was well loved by my teachers. As a reward, they gave me more responsibilities and extra duties. Every class day started with prayer followed by a "Mussolini" salute. As one of my duties I would lead my classroom in this daily salute. Raising our right hands just like the Nazis, we would shout "Viva Il Duce!".

The one responsibility which filled me with the most pride was to be the leader of the school's marching band. My uniform was black, red and white, representing the Fascists' colors. I wore a black, short, pleated skirt, a white blouse with the Fascists' insignia embroidered on it and a black ribbon tied in a bow around my collar. This was complimented by a matching black jacket. The jacket's long sleeves were festooned with two emblems; a Fascist's insignia near the shoulder and below this, another emblem indicating my position as the leader. I also wore black patent leather shoes with white knee socks, white gloves and the cutest little black beret. Complimenting my long blonde hair, I wore my beret on a slant which completed my leadership outfit, definitely standing out of the crowd.

With the support of my proud family and the entire town of *Perinaldo* behind me, I truly felt like a leader. Ironically, my name as well as my heritage was French. This made me feel even more superior to the others. For the first time I was glad for not being Italian and thereby considered unique.

My grandmother did not share my family's feelings, however. She was the only family member who was not proud that I was leading the school's band which promoted Mussolini's ideals. Mémé Catérina could never forget what the Fascists and Mussolini's followers had done to her husband. How dare they now choose me, her granddaughter, to lead a cause she abhorred. This was like a slap in her face and she made a point to openly show her outrage.

My grandmother would do everything possible to keep me from participating in any of the politicized school activities, parades and manifestations. Sometimes, she would lock me up in my room, insisting that it was a disgrace to use children for their own objectives. I would frequently be found in my room crying because I could not participate in the parades. This was when my mother was away.

When my mother returned, learning of Mémé Catérina's disciplinary actions, the two of them would be at each others throats. Olimpia would defend me, arguing that it was wrong to punish me for something I enjoyed. Although the family was against Mussolini and all he stood for and Mémé Catérina hated the Fascists, it should not have to involve me. "Do not forget," she would tell her mother, "Marie-Jeanne is French, she is not Italian. Did the school give her La Befana presents when the other kids always received

**Pié, Olimpia, Emma, Mémé, Honorine, Liliane.
Below: Lino and children - Danny, Richard and Jackie.**

them?" (La Befana is the Italian version of Santa at Christmas, celebrated January sixth.) "How many times has Marie-Jeanne come home crying because once more she had been left out due to the fact that she was French?" Olimpia would retort.

With my family's extreme bitterness towards the Fascists, Olimpia didn't want to attract attention to them. Being hostile could only bring us problems. Keeping a low profile would avoid any conflicts. Mémé Catérina, however, was very stubborn and irrational. She could not see that her rebellious attitude was putting her entire family and friends at risk.

Finally Pié, our next-door neighbor and friend, came over one evening and revealed to Mémé Catérina what she could not see. After this talk she continued to grumble but her animosity became much more subdued. Life went on. I continued to attend school with my cousins and managed to learn Italian as well as the usual subjects taught in elementary school.

Now added to us three girls' fear of ghosts was the fear of the Fascists which caused us to be even more cautious. One night going up to our bedroom on the third floor, we saw some little lights flickering in the gardens of "Castello Di Maraldi," the name of the astronomer Cassini's castle. Imagining that soldiers were out there, we assumed the lights to be the red glow off their cigarettes. When we girls told Mémé Catérina of the happenings across the road, she went to investigate. Returning with a large grin on her face, she retorted to us, "You little knuckleheads, *vous êtes fadades*! Those little lights are from harmless 'lucioles!' ". (Lucioles resemble little fireflies and are indigenous to this area

Although the Fascists had taken control of Italy's government long before

I was born, I was just beginning to realize the significance their power had over my family's life and Italy's populace. Still a child, my fantasy world of play was now being curbed with my new awareness of life's harsh realities.

Honorina, Emma and Henri, Zize and Joseph, Olimpia, Valerino and Claudette.

32

Another Life In Menton

I must have been close to seven years old when one day, while my mother was away my father reappeared. I could not say when I had last seen him. He may have been at "La Clinique Lanval" but I surely didn't remember.

He came to talk to me about Nini, about going to live with him in *Menton*, and about meeting my grandfather Jean and my grandmother Teresa. Describing his home and the life he led in *Menton*, he made it sound extremely wonderful and exciting. He tried to convince me to go back with him right then, but without success. Mémé Catérina showed him the door. "I'll be back!" he threatened.

Still a child, I could not see through his deception. Nonetheless, I was old enough to decide which parent I wanted to live with according to the Italian laws at that time. When my mother returned from her business trip, I approached her about my desire to go back to live with my father and meet my brother. Even though my mother was totally against the idea, she could do nothing but allow me to go. I was extremely excited. I thought I would be able to see my mother anytime and would meet my brother Nini. I didn't remember my brother who had left to live with my father when my parents separated and I was still just a baby. In short, I thought I was going to live a fairy-tale life!

My father and I boarded the train in *Ventimiglia*, the closest town that had a train station. (*Perinaldo* had only bus services since it was just a little village). Upon our arrival in *Menton*, my hopes and dreams were shattered into a million pieces. My disappointment was beyond words. *Menton* and my new home were not at all as my father had described. The home was located in one of the valleys of the city called *La Vallée du Borrigo*, near a railroad trestle bridge. Trains would come and go all the time between France and Italy, crossing this bridge. Each time a train crossed, it would shake the house to no end. The *Rue du Borrigo* would pass under that bridge. When I went to "Groupe Scolaire Pour Filles", a nearby school or actually anywhere, I would have to cross it. If I went the other way, I would end up in the hills.

While living in *Menton*, still a child, I was forced to grow up overnight. I never had the chance to play since I was always needed to help my ailing grandmother, Teresa, with the household chores. Due to my serious childhood illness, I was not always well myself. My father's urgency for me to live with him turned out to be for his own selfish interests rather than a sincere interest for his daughter. Having me live under his roof gave him a triple incentive.

Not only would I ease his household duties and allow him to take revenge on his estranged wife, he would also double his government allowance. According to the French laws, he could collect twice the "Allocations

Familiales" (a government supplement) by having both children reside with him rather than one.

Missing my mother and my life in *Perinaldo*, I was often sad and very homesick. I was never allowed to see or talk to my mother. Not having a phone, my mother would frequently try to visit me. Each time, she would be turned and sent away with a thinly disguised excuse without my knowledge. I would frequently ask my father if my mother had attempted to visit us. He always denied that she had come. Unaware of my mother's efforts, I felt even more lost and alone. Feeling estranged toward my father and my grandparents only added to my misery.

While my Grandmother Teresa was ill in bed most of the time, Grandfather Jean was an alcoholic and was always a little intoxicated. The two of them were constantly battling, causing the entire household to consistently be in an uproar! To top things further, my father was a salesman and was never home. I never felt so lost and all alone. How I wished to be back in *Perinaldo* with my mother where I truly belonged!

The house was filthy and dilapidated, with bugs and spiders which I just hated, and there was no electricity. Furthermore, the balcony of the house faced the dirty landscape along the railroad where people would throw their trash. I abhorred all the filth surrounding me, constantly feeling nauseated and often getting sick. The only positive thing about my decision in moving to *Menton* was the opportunity to live with my brother and get to know him. Nini was my only salvation and I adored him. He immediately was also enchanted with me, but sensed that I was very unhappy. He began to try to console me, not knowing what was wrong. Since he knew of no other way of living, he didn't realize the drastic change in my life, having to adapt to living in such a poorly run household. He assured me that he would help me do whatever was needed to make me happy. It was then that I realized that God plans things for us. If this was what he planned for me, so be it.

I tried to keep my mind busy with school work and household chores since they were escapes from my new, depressing family life. I also spent most of my free time with my brother and became closer to him than either of my parents, due to his intelligent and very protective ways. He became my closest friend and confidante. I would confide my secret ambitions and dreams to Nini. For one reason or another he was never very receptive. Perhaps being older he could see that some of my dreams were likely to be just that and impossible to ever realistically happen. Nini encouraged me to be less ambitious, to set my goals at an attainable level. All around us was poverty and depression. Rumors of war circulated and grew with each passing day.

In school I had to start learning French. Since my three years of previous schooling were in Italian schools, I was lacking in French. Because I was more advanced than my classmates in Italian and the other academic subjects, the teachers finally decided to place me in a special French class. For six months I concentrated on French only, eliminating all of the other classes. When I finished this class, the teachers still had difficulty deciding what grade they should place me in. They continued to switch me from class to class. First they started me in classes with students my own age, finding out quickly I was too advanced for this. Being promoted to a higher grade, I finally remained in the very advanced classes with students older than myself.

With school being a diversion from my unhappy home life I excelled rapidly, becoming one of the most brilliant students in the school. Studying with my older brother also gave me an extra advantage. He was 4 years older than I, so his homework was much more advanced than mine. Late at night I would sit for hours at the kitchen table with Nini, doing homework. He would not only help me with my French and academic subjects, but he also began to teach me English.

I would watch and learn from him while he did his assignments. With nothing better to do, I even studied Morse code with him. Nini took this course in school because he wanted to become a radio operator with the Air Force. I became very well informed in these subjects and all of this intense study later paid off for me.

I especially liked it when he studied English, because he would give me lots of vocabulary to study. In a couple of years school would require me to take English, along with French and another language of my choice. Already very advanced in Italian, English was the only other language and subject I had to learn and master. Wanting to be ahead of the game, I had the opportunity to learn it from my brother before I started to take it in school. This was a chance I wasn't about to let pass by.

Nini could never emphasize enough to me the importance of taking English in school the first chance I had. Little did he know that this determined little girl had already planned and made this decision. I had decided that mastering the English language would be my key to unlocking the door to all of my dreams and ambitions.

I had very few opportunities to play, although going to the beach, "Les Sablettes," with my brother was one of the highlights of my childhood. I remember "Les Sablettes" was one of the most popular and nicest beach in *Menton*, and I loved to go with him. This beach was unique because one could walk a long way out before the water finally rose above one's knees. The beach was always overflowing with children and I loved the smell of the Mediterranean waters. Being surrounded by fish and other fascinating sea life while I was treading water totally amazed me. Nini told me that the best way to catch fish was to put salt on their tails. Cupping my hands, I would pick up the salty sand and tried to drop it on the fishes' tails as they swam by. After many unsuccessful attempts I gave up, having come to the conclusion that my brother's idea was absolutely insane. He liked to tease me and was forever playing tricks on me. On the other end, I believed everything he told me.

On this particular day I had ventured a little further than usual. I did not know how to swim and was walking along the shore with water reaching my waist. I was looking at the bottom of the sea for seashells which I dearly loved.

The Blue Ring

I was careful to keep my distance from the crabs that would crawl all over the rocks and sometimes at the bottom of the sea. They reminded me of spiders which I abhorred, intensifying my fear of these strange creatures.

Knowing my terror of crabs, my brother would often tease me by swimming under water and pinching me, pretending to be a crab. That day was no different; he swam unnoticed and pinched my toes. Assuming it was a crab I screamed and lost my balance. Reacting to my brother's sneaky moves, I fell in the slimy and slippery sand, tried to pull myself up, but the sand and the seaweeds would not allow me to stand up. To add to my problem I had fallen into a deeper sand trap. I panicked. Thinking I was playing a game with him and not realizing my real danger, my brother kept on swimming. Someone, finally noticing my peril, swam to my aid. To this day I don't know how I ever survived and my fear of the deep waters has never left me.

Occasionally Nini and I would go downtown to purchase school supplies. This would give us a chance to see a different sight of *Menton*.

Located nearest to the Italian border, *Menton* is one of the most beautiful cities on the *French Riviera*. The shops are incredible; an absolute paradise for tourists with all its luxurious offerings.

The architecture is both modern and ancient, with a charm of its own. However, nothing can compare to its gardens; to describe them one only has to visualize the Garden of Eden.

A magnificent foliage decorates the many beautiful parks and covers vast areas of hillside and patches of undeveloped land in the blaze of indescribable color.

A delicate balance of sea air and fertile soil make this area unique. Any flora and fauna that can be imagined can be grown and found here.

Vast amounts of lemon and orange trees alternately planted alongside the city's main streets adds to this illusion. The euphoric scent from these colorful trees makes it one of the most fragrant cities on the *French Riviera*. *Menton* is noted for its citrus orchards and especially for their famous orange marmalade and orange blossom tea. The blossoms and fruit from these trees are used to adorn the splendid floats in their many parades. Once a year, their largest parade is *"Festival et Bataille des Citrons"* (The Festival and the Battle of Lemons). During the parade the girls on the floats would throw little cotton lemons and fresh lemon flowers to the spectators on the sides. This well known event held in *Menton* attracts hundreds of tourists and visitors each year.

Some nights my grandparents and my brother would take an evening stroll with me. Our favorite place to walk was down the main intersection called *Avenue Carnot* (named after a past French president) and in the gardens called *"Le Jardin Biovès"*, located in front of the "Casino Municipal". It is still known as the most spectacular garden in the city with its impeccable landscapes of every kind of exotic flower and plant imaginable. Countless numbers of lemon and orange trees and numerous magnificent statues and fountains made this a popular place for the locals as well as the tourists to gather and enjoy its beauty, even today. Families with children, however, could sometimes be a real nuisance with all of their screaming and running around.

Directly across the street from *"Le Jardin Biovès"* is the "Casino Municipal". Throughout my childhood I always wanted to visit this famous attraction. The "Casino Municipal" was an entertainment center known for its magnificent rooms filled with a variety of restaurants, nightclubs, gaming rooms, exclusive boutiques, and a splendid theater. Ideally located along the sea coastline, near *Promenade du Soleil* the casino has two spectacular views: the Mediterranean on one side and the luscious gardens on *Avenue Carnot* with the Alps on the other.

I would sit on a bench directly across from the entrance of the Casino and would dreamily stare at the fancy, chauffeur-driven cars that would pull to the curb and stop. The chauffeurs would hold open the doors to allow the rich and glamourous passengers to step out. The women would be dressed in their most lavish gowns followed by the gentlemen in dashing tuxedos. They would all proceed to the entrance of the Casino. Bellboys would be in attendance on each side of the Casino's entrance. Resplendent in white gloves and maroon bolero jackets, they would escort the dignified guests in. As the doors were opened, brilliant light from all of the chandeliers would flood the lobby. The Casino had numerous, beautiful salons where people would stroll and mingle. There were plenty of gift shops, dining rooms, banquet rooms and an enormous ballroom. Their theater, where performances took place featuring stars from all over the world, was one of the Casino's main attractions.

I would then direct my attention to the night sky searching to find a falling star to make a wish. I always made the same one - to someday be one of the ladies in the lavish evening gowns, escorted by a handsome man and admired by the crowd in the gardens. I made a promise to myself to someday have that become a reality.

.....

At one point it seemed that my father was at home more regularly. He also started to bring pamphlets and single sheets of propaganda material which he divided in little stacks, then turned them over to other people involved and they in turn would deliver to residences or wherever they were meant to be. When my father would leave the house, Nini and I would search to find out what all this propaganda was about, but my father would never leave a single trace of information behind.

Then one night, someone had forgotten to apply the red rubber stamp on this important promotional material. So my father asked us to stamp this emblem on these papers for him. Without hesitation, both my brother and I jumped at this opportunity to finally learn the secret information that was so carefully kept from us. We tried to discreetly read the material as we did our job of stamping. To our dismay we learned very little since this material was some special code that only the "inside people" could understand. From what we could make out, the informants from some organization were trying to warn the French people that they were in some very great peril. Some of our own people were conspirators that reported all our movements to the Germans. These same spies were "so-called French friends" that would act unconcerned, inviting everyone to drink with them and telling them, "Relax, there's no danger. This would never happen to us." In short, this propaganda was informing the French people that instead of hiding and thinking the danger will go away, they should prepare themselves because everyone was definitely in very serious danger.

Even though the other people involved could do this job of stamping, for about a month Nini and I continued to stamp the material. This saved my father an extra trip so he would bring all of it home, avoiding the danger of carrying the material around back and forth. After about a month, the stamping became a very natural thing, part of our regular evening routine. We learned to put it in small stacks, making the job much easier.

Then one night father told us that he had no one to deliver the material so Nini volunteered. Father said, "No, Nini. It's too dangerous. You are too young and I don't want you to go alone." I promptly interjected, "I'll go with him!" (As if this was going to take care of everything). I was then between seven and eight years old. Our grandparents never had much to say, but that night father turned us down. Later, however, he must have thought it over because the next day he approached Nini and I. He asked us all kinds of questions and he concluded that the two of us, being kids, would get away with this a lot easier since we would be the least suspected. Security was beginning to be more tight. Even the people we believed were our friends were acting as informants. So two to three times a week Nini and I would finish our homework (we never stopped our lessons), stamp and prepare the usual propaganda material and then we would head out to different directions only known to Nini prior to us leaving the house. This routine lasted for another couple of months. I can recall that it was very warm along the *French Riviera* so it must have been during the months of June and July. Then in the first week in August suspicions arose and we had to stop making all of our deliveries. Thinking that we were reasonably safe, Nini and I were unaware of our danger. When we had began our deliveries father had instructed and cautioned Nini to be on guard, keeping an eye on me at all times, and always look behind his shoulder. Without letting us know, father decided to follow us occasionally to make sure his suspicions were unfounded. At first we seemed safe, then he thought someone was following us. When he first suspected this, he admitted he was not sure, however, a suspicious shadow began following him home on several occasions. After this continued to happen a couple of times, he became definitely sure that his suspicions were justifiable. We stopped our deliveries immediately.

The Evacuation

After several weeks of suspense where tension was building up, the rumors of war became reality. At daybreak on September 1, 1939, the German Armies poured across the Polish border and converged on Warsaw. There had not been a declaration of war from Germany to Poland. This was the worst act ever to take place in history. German warplanes roared toward their targets destroying Polish troops, ammunition dumps, bridges, railroads and open cities, killing soldiers and civilians alike. This caused a terror which would last the next six years. England and France, very much unprepared, honored their obligations to Poland: England declared war on Germany around noon September 3, 1939, and France did the same a couple of hours later.

Meanwhile Il Duce (Mussolini) had made a promise to the Fuehrer to be on Germany's side, but found it hard to follow through due to the fact that Italy was lacking ammunitions, armies, and most of all, support from its people. According to Count Ciano they were not at all ready and it would take another two years for them to be able to survive. Mussolini was also afraid of France, because at this time the French Army was far superior to the Italian Army. Besides this, with Italy bordering with France, no one on either side of the border would fight if Italy went to war against France. For example, my family on my mother's side, the Pizzios, had all left Perinaldo, Italy and were in France working. The youngest son of the Pizzios', Valerino, was the only exception. He was drafted. Valerino would not fight his brothers, however, who were just across the border, so Mussolini sent all of the residents of the Italian Riviera (like Valerino) to Russia to help the Germans. Catérina Pizzio was the only one left alone in Perinaldo.

History will tell that the French were better prepared than the English, however, both thought that the Germans would never be able to cross the famous "Ligne Maginot". They never dreamed that the Germans would take all the small countries around it and just walk into France without even touching the famous defense line.

Even though Italy had not declared war on France, when the hostilities started in 1939, everyone down deep considered Italy as an enemy. Everyone was aware of the pact between Mussolini and Hitler and they knew he had pledged his entire support to the Fuehrer. Perhaps not everybody, however, was aware of the fact that Mussolini was really a coward. He easily made promises but when it came to keeping them he was really trying to be on the winner's side. Evidently he had some doubts since he tried, as it so often happens, to walk the thin line by trying to keep in good standing with both sides which ended up costing him a lot.

All things considered, France immediately prepared itself for an invasion from Italy as well as from Germany All the bridges, roads, railroad crossings and various strategic accesses were manned with sentries posted around the clock. The bridge near our house had been mined for several months when the rumors of invasion had started. This bridge was a very important one. The "Orient Express", the "Blue Train", the Pullman trains, and all the other main trains would have to cross this bridge, every day and in every direction. These trains would travel all across Europe.

I remember when I had to cross under the bridge to go to school I would cautiously look at the sentry, then at the sides of the bridge. After my inspection was finished and I felt safe enough to dare to cross, I would run across and heave a sigh of relief on the other side as if I had expected the bridge to blow up. Being just a child I used to dread crossing this bridge, quivering in terror every time it would shake from the moving trains. I even had nightmares about using this bridge, fearing that someday I would be blown up. How I dreamed for the day when I would not have to cross this bridge anymore.

The world's turmoil was taking place in *Menton*, on the *French Riviera*. It was the first town on French soil, close to the Italian border. So it happened that when France declared war on Germany in September of 1939 following the footsteps of England, my brother and I were getting ready to start school again. All of this came to a stop when the borders of Italy were closed and all business stopped as of September 3, 1939.

Within three hours of the war's declaration, we were to evacuate the city. At three o'clock (15:00 hour), the people who had not left the city and had no place to go, were advised that evacuation was necessary and would begin at the 18:00 hour. This gave us only three hours to prepare for our evacuation that the officials had ordered. We were assigned to a special location where we would board a Red Cross truck. We were further instructed that we should pack only the bare necessities and we were only allowed one suitcase. It was strongly recommended that only light items should be packed because we would be required to carry our luggage. We were also informed that we would be doing a lot of walking. Hastily, we each packed a small suitcase with our possessions. Since grandmother Teresa was ill, I followed her instructions and packed her suitcase for her. I however, was left with my own packing and I did an awful job! Instead of taking the essentials such as coats, boots, sweaters, socks, etc., I took things of sentimental value. At this time it was summer on the French Riviera so I wore sandals and very light clothing. Living on the Riviera who would have suspected that we would need warm winter clothing in early September. This proved to be a decision I would later regret. I was not prepared for the hard times I was about to face.

We had no idea where we were being evacuated to, how long we would be there, or what evacuation really entailed. Being naive, I assumed this was all very temporary and that we would be returning home soon. Ironic as it may sound, I actually looked forward to leaving since I dreaded our home and facing my everyday routine of crossing that terrible bridge.

Unfortunately Nini did no better than me when it came to packing his suitcase. Like me, he also packed sentimental items rather than the essentials. Among the belongings Nini packed were many items that were of no real practical use, but that were special to our family, especially my brother and I. Grandfather had many medals that he gave to Nini which he had received from past accomplishments including "La Croix de Guerre", "La Legion d'Honneur", and many other foreign medals. He also had quite a collection of documents he had received for his many personal achievements from different countries. Our family used to spend hours looking and talking about them.

Perhaps the most important medal was his Coat of Arms which all "Blue Blood" wore to show their title. This was a truly magnificent medal. It had three distinguishable patterns and symbols. The first upper left section was a pattern of silver and black that resembled a checkerboard. The upper right hand corner had thin red and white vertical stripes with one thick light blue stripe horizontally crossing it with a gold-figured eagle below. The entire bottom half of the Coat of Arms was two sets of gold torches on a solid blue background.

What interested me more than any of the medals which my brother adored was a blue ring that my grandfather wore. When he had run away years ago, he left the ring behind knowing he was giving up his right to it and everything it entailed. Therefore the ring went from one brother to another. Somehow down the line his parents forgave him and had their "notaire" (lawyer) look for him. This was not easy however, since he had changed his name. Finally he was located just two years before World War II began. The lawyer sent the ring with some documents explaining the request made from his now deceased parents regarding his inheritance. His family had no money left; however he did inherit the blue ring the medal "Coat of Arms" and its title.

This ring was passed down through the generations as the title was continually handed down. When my grandfather handed down this title, however, he avoided giving it to his eldest son, Gerard, of whose behavior he greatly disapproved. He also bypassed his other sons Vittorio and Armando, who had grown apart from the family. Furthermore it was known that Pietrina, his daughter, was crazy about the ring but because of the tradition the ring could only be handed down to a male heir. Therefore his grandson Nini was the next in line to inherit the title and wear the blue ring. From the day he received it I never saw Nini remove it from his finger.

This was no ordinary blue ring. It was so different and eye-catching. Every time that one would look at it they would find another interesting detail. Not to mention the magnificent workmanship or the real intrinsic value of the ring. This blue ring was the identical figure seen on the bottom portion of the Coat of Arms I described earlier. Like that medal, it had two gold torches engraved on the top but from a distance, when the light shone on them, they resembled snakes. The blue stone would also consistently change colors depending on the lighting. Even more intriguing, the ring opened up and there was a small, secret compartment.

Grandfather told us that when the "nobility" wore this type of ring and they were in fear of being killed or taken prisoner during a battle, they filled the secret compartment of the ring with cyanide in order to kill themselves before their enemy did, trying to get secret information from them. I would have nightmares about this. It upset me so much that Grandmother Teresa would scold Grandfather Giovanni (as she often called him) for scaring the children, me in particular, whether these were true stories or not. So my grandfather changed his story telling us that pictures of loved ones were placed in the ring's secret compartment for sentimental value.

Later I never got the chance to see the medals again. I did however see Nini wearing the ring at all times. In the beginning Nini would have to wrap a lot of black tape around the inside to prevent it from falling off. Since he inherited this ring at a very early age, his fingers were not thick enough to hold such a large ring yet.

Early that same evening, we joined the rest of the people from the city waiting to board the Red Cross trucks that were ready to evacuate us from *Menton to Cannes*. My father had already left to join his unit. What a sad group we all were. Just two elderly people and two children locking the door, leaving behind the few belongings we cherished. It was Indian summer and the weather was delightfully warm. I remember leaving behind a beautiful, warm coat with a fur collar that my mother had made for me. At that time, who would have taken a coat in such wonderful weather? Besides, riding in the truck I may have gotten it dirty. I told myself that it would be there when I got back, so I had thought, but we never returned.

It took us forever to board the trucks and vans. After what seemed like an eternity had passed, we finally left in a large caravan. The confusion was so incredible that it took several hours to finally arrive in *Cannes*. Everyone was leaving the border and it was like an Exodus. It was midnight when we finally reached our destination.

The authorities were far from being organized. Everything happened so suddenly that no one was prepared. Everyone was in a state of shock. Since the Red Cross personnel were completely disorganized, (they evidently had not believed that something like this could happen) no one knew what to do. The people had to stand long hours in the street before they were finally assigned to one of the hotels which had been requisitioned for that purpose. Finally our family was put up in the "Hotel Miramar", next to the famous "Carlton Hotel", on the Promenade de la Croissette. However it was not until the early hours of the morning and we were exhausted. We had been lost in a sea of frightened people screaming, crying and yelling. It was the epitome of nightmares.

Thus overnight we became a close target and in a very dangerous position. If Italy were to declare war, all the bridges between the two countries would be blown up. My family was in an uproar, the world was in utter chaos, and war was on its way. We did not know where we were going, nor where my father was. We remained in *Cannes* for two days, with the Red Cross doing the best they could under the circumstances.

Cannes and the Carlton Hotel on the left.

On the third day, we were put on a train headed for *Perpignan* in the *Pyrenées*. The *Pyrenées* are a chain of mountains dividing France and Spain. From *Perpignan*, we were taken by truck again to a "hameau" (a very small town) on the top of the mountains. With the wind blowing and the snow being over two feet deep, my family and I nearly froze to death. Here I was, wearing a blouse and sandals. To make matters worse, I was carrying a bag of useless items. As long as I live, I will never forget the bitter cold I had to endure.

We were lodged in a type of hangar that was extremely drafty. The authorities had laid several army cots, each with a single blanket. Nini and I went out and tried to find wood to light a small fire in the hangar, but the snow was so high that we found absolutely nothing. The few people that lived in the "hameau" were very unfriendly and suspicious by nature. Even though in actuality it was only two days, it seemed that we stayed there forever. I will never forget the deep penetrating cold!! Tolerating that constant frigid and damp feeling one had, with no relief, nothing warm, no heavy clothing, no hot food, not even wood to burn, it would seem like it lasted a lifetime for anyone who had to endure this. Our only salvation was one skimpy blanket per cot.

Then the Red Cross came back and moved us again to another "hameau" at a lower altitude. The cold was not quite so bitter, but there was still a lot of snow. However they brought more blankets and also some warm clothing for all of us. The lodging had improved a little but was basically a replica of the first one. Unlike our first lodging, we had a stove and had some wood to burn.

We remained at this "hameau" a week.

We still had no idea where my father was so Nini was in charge. I was always right behind him, trusting him completely and here he was, just a child himself! Poor grandmother, who was feeling very poorly throughout this ordeal, managed to survive. She, however, worried continuously about all of us since she felt so helpless. Unable to do anything herself, she just kept praying to God. Grandfather spent most of his time being angry at the world and it was not easy to tolerate his sporadic outbursts. I guess he was releasing his anger at not being able to have his bottle of daily booze like he had back in *Menton*.

We really had to fend for ourselves. We had no money and no provider. The Red Cross had done as much as possible. Once again they moved us to yet a lower altitude. This time it was a little village known as *Vernet-les-Bains*. This small town, a "Station Thermale", was known for its mineral water and baths. They also specialized in physical therapy and massages. It was extremely popular and people from all around would come to drink their waters, soak in their baths, and take part in the therapy sessions and massages they had to offer. These services were all provided in a large building with five hotels and seventy-five villas known as the "Station Thermale de *Vernet-les-Bains*". The town was deserted in the winter, but with its busy summer tourist season, they managed to survive. With the war, however, there would not be a normal summer tourist season anymore.

The older part of the town was built on a rock with the church in the center at the very top. For some reason it brought back memories to me of when I was living in *Perinaldo*, which was built very much the same as *Vernet-les-Bains*. Upon our arrival in this little town, a feeling of longing hit me. How I wished I was back living with my mother in *Perinaldo*! At that moment, I truly loathed my father and living with his family. Then, however, one look at my brother and all my hate dissipated and I felt fortunate that I had finally had the chance to spend time to get close to him.

Our lodging in *Vernet-les-Bains* was rather dilapidated and located in one of the poorest neighborhoods of the town. The only agreeable thing about our house was the view. From the south window, one could look out and see a small creek which ran down from the top of the mountain through a beautiful valley where hotels and villas had been built next to the thermal springs.

The interior of the house, however, was another matter. The kitchen, which was on the ground floor, had no window and the bedrooms were upstairs. These narrow stairs were on the verge of collapsing at any minute. Moreover, we had no electricity. The house had a depressing, dark, foreign and unfriendly atmosphere and was extremely dirty. The last problem Nini and I could handle so we immediately began cleaning and making it be as livable as possible. Because of grandmother's health problem, we decided that it would not be wise for her to climb the dangerous stairs to go to bed at night. So we managed to place a cot in an "alcove", a corner on the ground floor. When it was cold in the olden days, the residents of this home would sleep next to the kitchen near the stove to stay warm, that is if they had or could find wood to burn.

Soon after we adjusted to our new living conditions we settled down to a regular routine. Fortunately we were getting some kind of compensation from the government and shortly after living there Nini found a job. Unfortunately, the people here were just as unfriendly as they had been in the other lodgings where we had previously stayed. The natives were afraid that us refugees would take their food and their jobs since both were very sparse at this time. Having a slight grudge towards us, the residents of this village somehow felt that we were partly responsible for their market's shelves being completely bare now. According to the people, three weeks before our arrival, their shops were moderately stocked with groceries.

After overhearing many of the conversations of the townspeople, I later found out that the reason the markets were now so sparse was not just because of the war and the arrival of us refugees. The shopkeepers themselves had taken much of the food supplies and had hidden them for their own use. They even would bury cans of food in the ground. Time went on and food and work were becoming more scarce with the war constantly controlling our lives. Since our family had no providers, my father was discharged from the army and allowed to come home and take care of all of us.

As if the war were not enough, that particular spring when the big snow began to melt, it flooded the entire area. The little creek became a large roaring river dragging everything in its wake: trees, cattle, horses, barns, homes, carts, wagons, anything that got in its way. The homes along the creek were immediately evacuated. It was absolutely appalling to see the water seeping under these homes and buildings and in moments, the entire foundations entirely collapsing, just like a game of cards. Petrified, we watched from our house on the side of the mountain, five hotels, the "Station Thermale" and many villas disintegrate and be washed away by the overflowing waters. Finally, after the water levels continued increasing, the government officials sent flood specialists and more workers to help manage these uncontrollable waters. Unfortunately, our family was also advised that our building was no longer safe and that we should evacuate to the church. Once again we proceeded to pack what little belongings we had and up to the church we went. The climb was so steep that Grandmother had to be carried up. We remained in the church for four days, sleeping on army cots and waiting.

At last the floods ended and we were allowed to return to our house after the foundations had been thoroughly inspected. The result was devastating! The "Station Thermale", five hotels, and approximately fifty-five villas were destroyed. Some, entirely to the point of no repair. Cattle had been killed and crops had been destroyed causing even more scarcity of food. After these floods, diseases also came into the picture. In particular, one rare unknown disease which was caused by rotting trash and lack of purified water became the biggest concern. Medical treatment and medications, especially antibiotics to fight off these diseases, were just as limited as the food supply. With many people suffering from these illnesses, panic began to overtake the little village. To top this off, the resentment that the residents had for us refugees got worse instead of better.

Before long, Grandmother Teresa's sickness worsened and she had to be hospitalized immediately. We had to get an ambulance and rush her to the nearest hospital which was in the town of *Perpignan*. Being such a small village, *Vernet-les-Bains* did not have a hospital.

Two weeks after Grandmother Teresa was admitted into the hospital, it was my turn. I no longer could cope with the adult pressures surrounding me; the stresses we had faced since the onset of the war were just too much for me to bear, not to mention the perpetual bitter cold and dampness. The recent disastrous floods were the final blow and my immune system could no longer resist the obstacles I had to deal with daily. The lack of food and purified water caused me to again be under-nourished.

The doctor ordered me to be taken to the hospital for further tests. After a week of undergoing all kind of examinations, the main doctor in charge of my case had a very long talk with my father. He explained that I needed care, a lot of it, and that because of my childhood sickness, I had to be twice as careful now. He continued by asking where my mother was and did she know about my condition; this was taking place in my room while I was watching and listening to the entire conversation. My father was very uncomfortable and the doctor became very stern when he said: "This is extremely important, everything else is secondary."

Father, however, was not too happy about having to face my mother. He did not want to give her the satisfaction that he had failed in taking care of me, so he took another approach. Since my mother only kept in contact with Marise, his youngest brother's wife, he chose to have her directly contact my mother about taking me back to live with her.

Another Family Crisis

I remember my mother telling me about her past relationship with my father's side of the family. Some in this family, descendants of blue blood, played the part grandly. Throughout my mother's marriage there had always been some tension between the Vella family and herself. She found that no matter how hard she tried, she was completely ignored. Therefore she decided to forget them all; except for Teresa, her mother-in-law, she had no contact with any of them. She thought that perhaps their unreceptiveness was due to the fact that her descent was of a lower class. Later however, she learned that this seemed to be their normal behavior. The Vella's children never communicated with each other or with their parents after they grew up and moved away from home. This was the reason I never really got to know my father's family.

During my stay in *Menton*, however, I had the opportunity to talk with Grandmother Teresa at length. She would tell me of her growing up years on the Island of Malta and would describe each of her children, expressing her feelings about them. She confided in me; she was very unhappy.

Aaron, who used his middle name Gerard (my father), was the eldest son. He was very ambitious and very demanding as a child. She said the word "difficult" was a very appropriate description for him. Yet he had a heart of gold. This was best proven when he took care of his parents while all of the other children in the family had more or less forgotten them.

Then came Vittorio, the second son. According to Grandmother Teresa, he was a very studious boy and never caused them any trouble. He was very intelligent. Strangely enough however, after he married, having two children and a very successful career, he kept little contact with the family. In fact, I myself met him only once in *Menton*, rather briefly.

Next in line was Pietrina their only daughter. Unlike her brothers who were slim, tall and quite handsome, she was very short, heavy and not so attractive. She was rather a rebel and when she left home this did not change. She had strong convictions about people as well as politics. She married a heavy-set Italian man, and they had three daughters. They lived in *Menton/Garavan*, the closest community to the border of Italy. The reason she chose to reside there was because of her job. She was employed by the Custom and Immigration Service, whereupon she would allow or restrict one to cross the French/Italian border.

I later found out that before the war began, Pietrina had been the one responsible for not permitting my mother, who was still living in Italy at that time, to enter the French border when she tried to come and visit me. Whenever my mother was successful in crossing at different points of the border she and my father always managed to turn her from both Nini and myself. While I was living in *Menton* I had always wondered why I never saw or heard from my mother; now I knew.

The last child of the Vella family was Armando, the baby of the family. The two brothers, my father and he never got along. One reason for this was because they were both so much alike. Armando was a sharp dressing flamboyant playboy who tended to like the girls a little too much and lived in the fast lane, like my father. He seemed to be very successful, but no one knew how he made his living. He married Marise, an attractive brunette who was very well educated and "down to earth". I liked and admired her very much.

While living in *Nice, France* they had a son. Marise was a wonderful mother and wife and had so many qualities, but to everyone's dismay, Armando continued to be the same flamboyant playboy and never changed his ways. Although Marise cared very deeply for him, she could not deal with his fluctuating moods and sporadic behavior. She eventually divorced him. Marise was the only relative of the family that my mother liked and would converse with from time to time. They both got along so well probably because they both shared a similar situation: a bad marriage. My mother and Marise had dealt with their husbands and both had ended up divorcing them or in my mother's case separating. The two of them continued to keep in contact along the years.

So it was to be expected that my father, not wanting to face my mother, contacted Marise and explained his situation to her. Immediately she volunteered to contact my mother about my moving back to live with her and make all the necessary arrangements. The only thing she requested from my father was that when he would take me to her home, he would only provide transportation for me. She did not want him around. She knew there would be a very emotional run-in which could flare into a big battle. Without a moment of hesitation my father agreed wholeheartedly. He had no desire to meet my mother face-to-face, he knew what would happen, and must have been aware that he had it coming.

At this time my mother was no longer living in Italy. She had moved to *Marignane* to live with her middle brother Lino. The reason was she no longer worked as a governess for the family that had employed her for several years. When the war began, the family had to move back to their original home in the Netherlands. Although they tried to persuade my mother to come live with them and continue working for the family, my mother declined. She kept hoping and praying that somehow she would get me back to live with her. In her heart she knew that I would be back and she didn't want to be away when this opportunity arose. She had tried every way, not only to visit me but to have me back with her. She even contacted lawyers who could not help her, there were so many important issues to deal with, the entire country was in shambles. Moving to the Netherlands would be like giving up. She had to remain close not only for my sake but for my brother's as well.

My father delivered me to my Aunt Marise on a Wednesday night and as promised, he left immediately. Upon my arrival and seeing me, my aunt was taken aback at my sorry appearance. She had not seen me since my departure from Perinaldo. At that time I was a happy, healthy and well-groomed child. Now however, as I stood before her, she saw me as a poor child who was extremely thin and gaunt looking, with clothes all tattered and outgrown and my hair long and stringy. I really must have been a sight! The next morning my aunt promptly took me to the beauty shop to get my unmanageable hair that she said "looked like a mop", cut short. She told me she wanted me to make a good impression when I would first reunite with my mother. At last I was finally presentable to greet her.

I could not believe that this was finally a reality. I had not seen her for nearly four years. I also realized what my mother had gone through. She had not forgotten me, my father and my aunt were to blame. The last day I had seen her was before I boarded the train with my father. How deceitful and conniving he had been. Here I stood, a scrawny, emaciated girl who had struggled to stay alive and survive all the hardships of living, with a broken family, in the middle of a war.

The Blue Ring

Reuniting With My Mother

That afternoon, my mother and her brother Lino arrived by train from *Marseille* to pick me up. No words could express the relief and excitement of those long awaited precious moments when I saw my mother for the first time since my departure with my father from *Perinaldo*. It seemed to me that a million years had gone by since then! My mother had wanted to take Nini along with me as well but Marise told her that my father would never allow this. He told Marise to tell my mother, " Feel fortunate that you have Marie-Jeanne back. So run and take her home and take care of her!" Oh, how I despised him, especially how he treated my mother with such disrespect.

After a short visit with Marise, the three of us left for *Antibes, France*, a town on the *French Riviera*, approximately forty minutes from *Nice* by bus. There we were to visit my mother's youngest sister, Tante Zize. We had quite a family reunion! My mother bought me a new pair of brown shoes with wooden soles and imitation leather on top. I really felt like a queen. We remained

Emma, Olimpia my mother, Liliane, and Honorina my aunt.

Marie-Jeanne and Liliane.

with Tante Zize for a couple of days, then we went to Marseilles by train and then to Marignane by bus. Between the reunion with my mother, the new shoes and the wonderful train rides, I was in heaven!! I finally felt like I was at "home".

I was so happy to be back with my mother once again. *Marignane, France*, was a quiet little town in those days, located twenty miles from *Marseille*. The airport itself was located approximately a couple of miles from *Marignane*, in the opposite direction. Most of the people from *Marignane* worked for the *Marseille/Marignane Airport* in one capacity or another.

During their youth, my mother's two brothers, Pipo and Lino moved from *Perinaldo, Italy* to *Marignane, France* seeking a better way of life. They had worked very hard and had developed a reputable business as cabinet makers and specialized in various carpentry skills. Uncle Pipo was the owner of a villa where his family lived and also owned the workshop where they ran their carpentry business. This large warehouse was conveniently located behind the home. Whereas Uncle Lino, who was still single and had no family to support like Uncle Pipo, invested his money in the machinery which consisted of a considerable amount of expensive "state of the art" equipment. He even invested in the highly specialized apparatus that converted the unprocessed wood from tree trunks into sheets of wood. (At that time there were no lumber yards in *Marignane* where one could just buy the ready-made plywood, sidings, etc.)

Uncle Lino had an apartment in the downtown of *Marignane* which he shared with my mother and this is where I went to live. We lived on the third floor of the building which was located in the old part of town. At first, still very weak from my illness, I spent most of my time resting and trying to get healthier and stronger with the wonderful help of my mother. Even though there was a shortage of food at this time due to the war, my mother always tried to give me a warm nutritional meal, saving the best food that they could acquire.

After we settled to a normal routine in the apartment, my mother who had started a business of making fashionable clothing, resumed her career. Since she was a very skilled seamstress and creative designer, her business flourished even though the hardships caused by World War II never ceased. This was in 1941. France was divided, the north part was under occupation and the capital was *Paris*. We in the south supposedly were not to be occupied and we were under the regimen of *Vichy*, as capital.

Soon she had many young girls who came and learned from her and in exchange they would assist her with her fairly large cliente. These young girls were known as "Midinettes". The girls learned their craft and my mother earned a respectable income to help her fulfill her family's living needs. They would learn to sew by putting the finishing touches on the garments that my mother had completed. As they mastered this skill, they gradually would begin sewing and finally cutting during their apprenticeship. At this time they would earn a little money as a reward for their accomplishments in learning the trade. It would also give them an extra incentive to continue perfecting their skills.

My mother and the girls worked many long hours. I also was used to working long hours, either at home or at school. Now it was different living with my mother. I did not have the responsibilities I used to have in Menton. My mother and her brothers were very independent and extremely well organized. Moreover it was spring and school would not begin for me until the fall.

I had to do something useful with my time so I began helping my mother with her work. Everyday when the girls came to work, I would join them, doing the finishing work on their ongoing sewing projects. I loved to be around and listen to them chat. To me it was a refreshing change having these young students talking "girl talk". This was the only time one could escape the somber and serious people around us. Everyone was scared, overwhelmed and upset dealing with the unknown and making the best of it. No matter where you went, the entire community seemed to be holding their breath and jumping at every strange sound as if they anticipated some kind of bomb to go off at any given second.

I was the only one who seemed to be living in heaven. Don't get me wrong, I missed my brother terribly and I wrote him often. I also continued to study and practice the subjects that Nini had taught me, mainly coding and cryptography including the Morse code and English.

I did not however, miss anything else about my previous life in Menton. I had tried to get closer to my grandparents to no avail. I really never knew where I belonged. I am sure that my unhappiness, which was very obvious, was not very welcome and perhaps it was also my fault if our relationship was strained. Since I felt betrayed, I held everyone responsible. I didn't really know how miserable I had been until now. Living with my mother was like an ultimate dream, something I had taken for granted in my younger years while growing up in *Perinaldo, Italy*.

After the girls left for their respective homes, my mother would proceed to make some clothes for me out of her old ones, or from some leftover material. We would spend hours trying to figure out the least expensive way to do it and the quickest, because I was really in need of them.

The Blue Ring

Surviving The War

Due to the war my mother often worked in exchange for food rather than money. There was a big shortage of food and obtaining more than what our rations would allow was worth more than gold. I remember sitting at the dining room table and we had a single potato for the three of us, my mother, her brother and myself. There were times when all we could get was "mais", a kind of orangy corn that was normally just given to feed the chickens. What they sold us, however, was just the husk so we cooked them and it made some kind of mush. To this very day I won't eat corn!

Another time when I was sick, I recall my mother saying, "We just have to get some milk." The little milk that was available was given exclusively to the babies. Fortunately, one of our customers was a farm girl and she offered to pay my mother's dressmaking services by supplying her with fresh milk instead of paying cash. From time-to-time I would have relapses and would get extremely ill. The only nourishment I could handle was milk.

Desperately needing the milk offered, my mother agreed to the arrangement. The girl later returned with the material my mother was to use to create her dress. However she did not have the milk and said that she would bring it when the dress was completed. My mother worked late into the night to finish the dress. When the dress was finished and the milk arrived, my mother was stunned. To her dismay, it was only a very small bottle with barely six fluid ounces of milk which had been watered down. My mother who was livid with anger, kept her emotions inside. She did not yell at the farm girl but was extremely stern instead. I can remember hearing my mother scolding her, saying, "Only one mistake is ever allowed, and in our family, we never make the same mistake twice! God will take care of people like you!" Needless to say, that was the end of the farm girl.

Once more, my mother was approached to do a job for trade. Remembering what had happened with the incident of the farm girl and the dress she had made for the milk, my mother didn't want to do it. This time, however, she had no choice. An unknown lady had approach us offering to trade for bread. French people are big eaters of bread. Our rations only allowed us one single slice a day. During her introduction the lady mentioned her German boyfriend. Reluctantly my mother agreed. The next day when she brought us the material, she was escorted by a German officer carrying a round loaf of bread. Keeping as calm and acting as normal as possible my mother discussed the pattern and took measurements. The German handed her the bread and she pointed to the table nearby, pretending to be busy, not wanting to come in contact with him. Later she explained to me that she was on the verge of telling him to keep it, but decided otherwise. The bread was so hard that in order to eat it we had to soak it in hot water. We were hoping that this experience would not reoccur with the lady or any other mistresses of the Germans because we would have to sew whether they paid or not. Thank God this was the only time. That was payment enough in itself.

Due to the war there was a shortage of food. In order to obtain our small share we were allocated a certain amount of food stamps which permitted us to buy our necessities. We were given only a strict minimum of stamps which no one could ever possibly live on. Therefore, the black market was rampant. These stamps came in a sheet and when used, they would have to be counted and cut which was extremely time consuming, adding to the time we stood in the long lines. These limited amount of food stamps only allowed us to acquire food on the date that they would be distributed in our neighborhood. Whenever the distributions of food were announced, the town was in an uproar. The townspeople would scurry to acquire their rations, fearing that all of the supplies would run out before they could collect their share. There were long lines everywhere you went. Moreover, the food stamps that we would receive were only redeemable at certain markets.

The distributions of the various food supplies would take place only about once a week. Each week only certain items would be sold. It took approximately five to six days to distribute these goods to all of the people who were standing in the long lines to receive their share. Once all of the supplies from this particular distribution were dispersed, another one would then be able to start and so on. For example, if sugar was distributed on Monday, this sale would continue until Thursday. Then the sale for flour or potatoes would start on Friday and continue until Monday or Tuesday, etc. The only food distribution we would receive every week was bread.

There were many markets one would have to go to. This meant that one of the family members would have to stand in line for hours to purchase the supplies needed while another member would do the same at the other markets. The meat had to be bought at the butcher shop once a month, milk at a "laiterie", (a dairy farm) only for small children and the bread was bought weekly at the bakery. I spent most of my time standing in lines at Pilia's Grocery Store. Here we could buy most of our family's necessities such as sugar, flour, fruit and vegetable produce (when available), soap, and cooking oil. Eggs and cheese were so rare that they could only be purchased from the black market.

Standing in the long lines at Pilias Grocery Store became a normal and very monotonous routine. The two Pilias brothers were very old men who were both short and bald. These two brothers had owned this grocery store for many years. Charles Pilia was the main grocer while Cesar Pilia was the helper who worked the stockroom. Everything was purchased matching the amount of food stamps with the actual goods available that day and paying for them. It would take hours to make a purchase since the two old brothers were very slow and nit-picky. They were extremely fussy when they had to distribute the merchandise. They would meticulously cut the exact amount of butter or shortening allowed or would concisely measure the right amount of flour, pasta, sugar, etc. They were always afraid that someone down-the-line would not receive any if they ever gave over the amount allotted. They also had to count and cut the stamps and cash in the money. It always took forever.

One day Charles was all alone and he seemed terribly upset, so I offered to count and cut the stamps for him while he worked the cashier. He was utterly thankful and gave me some food that he had in the back of the store to show his gratitude. To my surprise, he gave me a very small amount of real coffee beans for my mother. Since the beginning of the war, coffee was a luxury. My mother, who adored coffee, would have to roast and ground any type of bean available and use it instead of coffee. When I arrived at home that night, my mother acted like a little girl who had just received her first doll.

Thus began a regular ritual. Even if I had already received my rations when a distribution came, Charles would send Cesar to come and get me at our apartment to help out if I could. I tried to help as often as possible because I would get some extra food which was always a great welcome. As the months went by, I graduated from counting and cutting the stamps to cashier. As I became more experienced and after a lot of thought, Charles decided to allow me to try my hand at actually cutting, measuring, wrapping and serving the various commodities to the customers. Before I knew it, I was doing it all. Sometimes Charles would even leave me to tend the store by myself. The Pilias also had a niece named Mary. She was a bit older than me and a very nice girl. We both would take turns working the store and soon we became very close friends. I have wonderful memories when I was working for the Pilias. My mother appreciated the little extra food I would receive as compensation for my work and I felt proud that I could somehow help the family during these hard times. Thank God the Pilias had hired me to work for them. It made the rough times a little easier.

In the spring of 1941, when I first went to live at the apartment in *Marignane*, the Germans had not yet begun to occupy the town. However we were constantly on edge with the many air raids we encountered. We had been instructed to carry our valuable possessions with us in a small suitcase. We were allocated gas masks (as Nini had predicted and had forewarned me) which we also carried with us. Often we were instructed to put these on so we would know how to use them when it was necessary. The smell was just awful.

Whenever "aircrafts" were detected, the sirens would go off and we were instructed to drop everything and go directly to the shelters. The public shelters were located on the outskirts of town, near open spaces. "Tranchées" (trenches) had been dug in the ground and covered with camouflage material, branches, or whatever could be used as a disguise. Each shelter had two entrances to avoid the bombs' impact.

Many people who owned their homes, however, made their own shelters near their house. These were built much the same as the public shelters; however, they were smaller. My two uncles Lino and Pipo built one of these personal shelters next to Pipo's villa. Like the other shelters, the trenches were camouflaged and there were also two entrances to protect us from the impact of nearby explosions that were most likely to occur near Uncle Pipo's villa. It was located a few hundred yards from the airport "as the crow flies". Uncle Pipo's shelter was different from the other shelters upon entering. Three or four steps below the trenches, there were benches on each side, a supply of water and blankets. On the ground, instead of dirt and mud, there were wood shavings which my uncles had in abundance. This kept the humidity down for the children when they would stay for long periods of time during the constant air raids.

When we first experienced air raids, usually nothing happened. After two or three hours the siren would signal the end of the "alert" and we could return to our normal lives, if one could call it that! It still amazes me to this day how the people could continue to make the best of their lives, acting as normal as possible even with all of the restrictions we were experiencing. Furthermore, we lived in constant fear that we would be struck from the air, always suspiciously looking around us expecting to see the Germans at any minute. This only added to the overall difficulties we faced with each passing day and night.

. . .

When the war was barely avoided in 1938, Uncle Pipo, concerned about his children, began to think of a way he could put some food aside. He started to buy canned food by the case and accumulated quite a large supply of condensed milk.

He owned a motorcycle to get around, as well as a bicycle, but his pride and joy was a collection of guns for which he had built a beautiful piece of furniture. Through an unbreakable glass door, one could see 12 guns displayed in an upright position, surrounded by a small group of hand guns.

This small "artillerie" was comprised of a couple of Mauser rifles, several "Lebel" rifles, 3 carbines and some unknown old rifles, probably dating from World War I, all kept in excellent condition. The hand guns were arranged on each side and they were Berettas, all different in some way, a Mauser, a Browning High Power and a "Lebel" 1892, probably a collection item.

The gun case was located in the entrance of the house and of course was locked at all times. It was the first thing anyone would see upon entering.

When the war was declared, Pipo, extremely resourceful, started to dig a shelter, with the help of Lino, next to his villa. Across from the shop and his property was a vacant lot which was bordered by tall shrubs on the inside, leaving open the area to the road. After the shelter was completed, and hearing of the disastrous circumstances and direction the war was taking, he decided to dig another hole about 3-feet deep between the shelter and the field. After putting wooden boards on the bottom, he added a layer of wood shavings, then neatly put all the cases of food he had accumulated in the hole, covered the entire stock with more wood shavings, more wood board, then replaced the dirt on top with all kinds of camouflage over the entire surface.

The next order of business was the guns. What to do with them? He then built an insulated trunk-type container and wrapped his guns in oil-cloth. After having them treated to avoid rust, each was wrapped in several layers, and all were fitted into the trunk.

Then the digging began again, this time in another spot more hidden. He did not plan to pull them out until the war was over, so they were buried. The last thing he had to do was to take care of the gun case. To his great sadness he had to change and alter entirely the look of it. The glass door was replaced by a wooden one, the interior was entirely remodeled, shelves were added where books were displayed.

People learned to become ingenious. As it turned out, the cases of food lasted about a year and a half. At least it helped the children in the early stage of their lives. When I came into the picture, after I was reunited with my mother, the supply was coming to an end. It had been used sparingly and no one ever mentioned the guns. But the "Resistance" was not borne as yet.

The Blue Ring

The German Occupation
The Birth Of The Resistance

On June 14, 1940, the Germans paraded into Paris. The city had been declared "ville ouverte" (open city). They rode their motorcycles and tanks with condescension, knowing very well the impression they were making on the Parisians, who stood and watched, paralyzed. Many French men and women wept with tears running shamelessly down their cheeks. Others stared with interest and curiosity.

The German armored vehicles advanced around the "Arc de Triomphe" and down the "Champs Elysees". All around the "Place de l'Etoile" armed German units with cannons as well, were in position. Their machine guns aimed down all of the avenues. The French officers who had dealt with the Germans regarding the surrender of Paris, had promised there would be no resistance. The Germans, however, found that hard to believe. They did not know the French mentality at all. Paris had capitulated without a single shot being fired. One thing that no one but a Frenchman would know was the fact that Paris has always been the symbol of France and its destruction should be avoided at all costs. Paris was an open book of history, arts, architecture and it was the heart of France.

Place de l'Etoile, Paris

Many of the people stood silently while the Germans were taking over buildings, replacing the French flags with the German ones. The French had their own idea of how they would get it back. They counted on the greed of the Germans to preserve our treasures, for that is when the game began. Everyone of the high ranking German leaders wanted these treasures for their personal use and were going to fight among themselves by trying to outdo one another. Whoever succeeded would have to take them out of France and that alone was the catch that allowed the French people much needed additional time.

They knew that the political struggles in government had seriously undermined our defenses, but the real truth was the fact that France's military was not prepared to fight in the open. Therefore the French swallowed their pride and proceeded to plan the next alternative.

On May 17, 1940 Premier Reynaud announced that Maréchal Pétain had joined his cabinet as vice-premier. Then on June 17, 1940, President Lebrun announced that he had asked Maréchal Pétain to take over the reins of government. Pétain had halted the Germans at *Verdun* in 1916 and had become a military hero in World War I. Things were different now, however; this was World War II, and Maréchel Pétain was old and feeble. That same day at 12:30, he stood up before a microphone to address the nation, speaking to the French people. He began talking in a quavering voice. Some thought it may have been because he was in the grip of deep emotion or simply finding himself against the wall and being full of worry. That may have been true, nevertheless most knew it was the voice of an aging man. A man who was too old to know what was good for France. Slowly he began, "I offer to France the gift of my person that I may ease her sorrow. It is with a heavy heart that I tell you that we must halt the combat. Last night I asked the adversary whether he is ready to seek with us, in honor, some way to put an end to the hostilities!"

This speech was received with contempt by the majority of the population. Pétain had sold us to the Germans or so this is what the country thought. France was gripped with emotions, between fear and fury and in some instances, relief. Some thought this meant the end of the war for us, not realizing it also meant the beginning of the nightmare.

Through this emotional state, the Resistance (which had been lingering like a phantom, not really knowing which way to go or who to trust with a million and one more questions tied to it) started to take shape. Many decided that they were going to continue to fight. This included General Gabriel Cochet, a former chief of the Deuxième Bureau (similar to the CIA), who was now commander of the Fifth Army Air Force. He held a meeting with his staff telling them, "Pétain is wrong. There is no hope of an honorable collaboration with Hitler." He then added, "We must at all costs continue to fight, but in our own way. We will have to learn to hide what we are doing, camouflage our movements and arms and help as many people as we can, to escape for now." The Resistance was born.

This, however, did not become official until June 18, 1940, at 6:00 p.m., when General De Gaulle spoke from London, England on the BBC (British Broadcasting Company). "Is the last word said? Has all the hope gone? Is the defeat definitive? No. Believe me. I tell you nothing is lost for France. This war is not limited to the unfortunate territory of our country. This war is a world war. I invite the French officers and soldiers who are in Britain or who may find themselves there, with their arms or without, to get in touch with me. Whatever happens, the flame of the French Resistance must not and will not die." His speech was directed to the military personnel, however it reached many civilians. It was as if war had been declared once more, but a different kind of war, not in the open. The reaction from the crowds was electrifying! I believe this speech started the fire that was to burn underground until V-Day.

At the time the BBC station was not very well known and no one knew if it would reach out into France. It didn't matter however, because the ones who listen to General De Gaulle's speech told those who had not heard it. His message spread like wildfire and soon all of France knew what was happening. Moreover, at this time the pamphlets and notices began to circulate. Living in *Menton* at the time, Nini and I had stamped many of these pamphlets which contained warnings to the French people of the events to come. For some reason however, most of the French believed that if they ignored the warnings, the problems would just go away.

On that day, an exodus began. All of the French military, making the crossing anyway they could, went to join General De Gaulle in England. At this time there were German U-boats already occupying the waters of France which was the direct route to England. The French soldiers in the south half of France could not go north to get to England since the Germans were now occupying the entire north of France including Paris. The only way the French Military could get to England was to cross Spain undercover disguising themselves (often as old women) and proceed by boat.

In the meantime, my father picked up where he left off. Again he went back to work for some produce company driving trucks. He delivered merchandise during the day and at night delivered supplies to the new FFI in the *Pyrenées* mountains. They were in great need of his help. The new FFI consisted of mostly young adults who were running and hiding from the Germans, fighting for France and lacking all of the essentials to survive. At first the groups were small, operating on their own but soon their strong will, determination and persistence to fight paid off and everyone that could, helped by furnishing ammunition, food and medication. However the most important help was the vital information and contacts so desperately needed by the FFI to anticipate their enemies next move. The headquarters for these groups became known as the "Maquis".

Perpignan was located on the *Mediterranean Sea*, close to the Spanish border and surrounded by the *Pyrenees* mountains where a tremendous amount of traffic was taking place. Spain was known as a neutral country and everyone wanted to go there. The defecting soldiers or political refugees could obtain false orders, identifications, and passports through the "safe houses" located all over France. Once in Spain, they would contact the Réseau de la Resistance and travel along the coast towards England. They would use fishing boats at night, remaining very close to the land and would then proceed using the darkness as their cover. During the day, they would hide in the most remote areas to resume their long journey as permitted.

Spain also had many "safe houses" and many travelers would use these to their advantage. Others even boarded hay wagons pulled by oxen while they stayed on the land, but would inevitably have to finish their journey by boat. The risks were prolific and chances of being caught by the Germans were more than likely. Cautionary measures had to be taken at all times. If arrested, the French had no choice. A German arrest would mean, at the least, deportation or facing the firing squad, depending on the circumstances when they were arrested and how the Germans felt about it. Even though Spain was not occupied by the Germans, Franco, the leader of Spain, was a Fascist like Mussolini and was friendly with the Germans.

The Resistance was the most incredible organization. It was built primarily by the hearts of the people of France. These people, wanting to help, gave, expecting nothing, sometimes losing their own lives for their beliefs, for integrity, decency and honesty.

Although the French had already considered the Italians to be their enemies in 1939, Italy officially declared war on France, June 10, 1940. The armistice which was signed with Germany, included Italy and took effect on June 25, 1940. According to this armistice, the north half of France with Paris being the capital, was to be occupied. While the south of France with Vichy serving as the capital, was to remain unoccupied. This however, was short lived.

That fall I enrolled in school and just loved it. I soon became number one and was voted President of the Students Organization. I was so happy finally that my personal nightmare had vanished in my mind. Being very involved with my studies helped enormously, distracting my attention from the hardships we had to encounter and made it easier to cope with the surrounding realities. For the time being I did not think of tomorrow but just lived day-to-day. School was now attended all year round from 8:00 a.m. until 6:00 p.m. with a short break from 12:00 noon until 1:30 p.m. Days followed each other in a monotonous way, with the feeling of being on hold.

Then one day we were told to stay inside, close the shutters and stay out of trouble. The schools were closed as well as all the shops and businesses.

The Germans were occupying the town which came to a standstill. To our knowledge there had not been any changes with the armistice agreement. However, Germany was known for invading, attacking or occupying without any warnings. I had been so miserable, cold and starving these past two years that nothing surprised me and the fact that our country was being occupied by our enemies, the Germans, had been expected. Actually, I really didn't understand what that implied.

Against my mother's orders, I opened the shutters slightly and saw from a distance the German convoys coming down the main street. It was like a parade with all of the Germans arriving. First there were the motorcades and motorcycles, followed by a multitude of cars and trucks of all kinds. There was not a French soul in sight.

Upon their arrival, the Germans took a look around and chose the best houses or villas to use for their headquarters and some homes for the living quarters of the officers. This invasion made our lives even more miserable. Adding to the problems we had already been facing, we now had to follow new rules. Sentries were placed at various points around the town, the airport and other critical check points. Anyone over 12 years old, had to wear an identification tag with a picture duly acknowledged by German authorities. The children who lived on the outskirts of town and nearer to the airport were required to wear the same identification tag starting at the age of ten. A curfew was also put into effect between the hours of 11:00 p.m. and 5:00 a.m. Every military personnel who had not been successful in escaping the area before its occupation were obligated to report to the German headquarters. If one failed to do so and was later caught, they would pay dearly. Most of the time these soldiers would be detained as prisoners of war and later would be sent to the camps in Germany for free labor. Moreover, no gatherings were allowed. My mother had to let her sewing helpers go believing the safety of the girls was in jeopardy. These girls were too much of a tease for the Germans since they were very attractive, young, nice and naive.

The air raids intensified and this time there was a lot of action. The airport, now occupied by the Germans, was being bombed by the Allied Forces on a regular basis. Either way, we seemed to be the target. The Germans gave us new rules to follow for everything. With the new curfew now in effect, when the alarm rang out, not one second before, we were to leave our homes for the shelters. My Uncle Lino almost got shot for stepping out before the sirens gave the warning. Whether it was from lack of vigilance or simply because the Germans just didn't care if the French civilians were caught in the middle of an air raid, it seemed that the signal from the siren was always too late. Whenever I heard the plane in the distance, I would wake up my mother and my uncle. We would then hurriedly get dressed, grab our pre-packed suitcases and wait for the signal inside our building doorway. At the sound of any air raid, my mother would be paralyzed in fear and I would end up carrying the light suitcase and dragging her along with me to move, while Uncle Lino, who was always ahead of us, would carry all of the rest of our baggage. After we became accustomed to the daily air raids, my mother decided to be more prepared for the next one. She wanted to take some additional personal belongings and strongly insisted that she would be able to carry her own suitcase. (During previous air raids, my mother and I had shared the same suitcase which I carried while Uncle Lino would carry some essentials that we all shared, besides his own personal belongings.) Since she could not make up her mind as to which suitcase to take, she took out two different sized suitcases from the closet and left them both open on the bed. Even though she finally packed the one suitcase that she wanted, both suitcases were placed near the door with the other pre-packed suitcases.

One time, Uncle Lino was away from the apartment for a few days as he was working on a special project with Uncle Pipo. Because the work was being done at the shop and required the two brothers to work late into the night, Uncle Lino stayed over at Pipo's villa until the job was completed. So for about a week, my mother and I had the apartment to ourselves. One of the nights that Uncle Lino was still away, the siren and the bombing started simultaneously. Fortunately, I was a light sleeper, so I heard the planes in the air long before the siren went off, therefore, my mother and I were already dressed and ready to go. Even though we were the first ones out, we didn't get too far. I could see that the Germans were already aiming at the Allied planes as they crisscrossed the sky, dropping bombs near the airport. At the same time the ground attack known as the "fire works" was also underway. There was no way we could possibly reach the shelters on the outskirts of town in time. To get to the shelters we had to take the "Cours Mirabeau", one of the main avenues of the town. So to avoid being an open target and hit, we laid in a nearby gutter which seemed like the safest place at the time. We laid there for what seemed like an eternity until the bombing and firing completely ceased. When we returned to our home, still shaking, we discovered that the suitcase my mother had been carrying was empty. She had picked up the wrong one in her haste; instead of laughing it off we realized how tense we were becoming, but then this had been a night to remember.

As these air raids continued to occur, sometimes two to three times the same night, our home seemed to be more unsafe than before. My mother kept saying this was a dangerous area and kept strongly insisting that it would be better for us to go to another shelter, possibly a safer one. Being the early ones out, sometimes we would reach some shelters first and mother would say "See, no one comes here, it is not safe". Then more people would start to drag in and many seriously injured from the cross fire. Unfortunately they would have to wait until the air raid was over. The Red Cross, which consisted of a limited group of volunteers, was located at the most critical points. Most of them had little medical knowledge. I began to get qualms about "shelters" and the entire setup. Where would a safe place be? I don't think that my family or I slept through an entire night without being disrupted with these awful air raids. I continually listened for planes; we were so close to the airport which was the main target for the Germans to attack, then later the Allied forces who would try to hit the Germans. It didn't matter which plane was in the air, we were never out of extreme danger and had to constantly run so we would not be the next victims.

To make matters worse, *Marseille* and the *Provence* have seldom seen snow but that particular winter all of the odds were against us. The snow and the Mistral winds were to last throughout that winter. Homes were heated by coal stoves, yet coal was a luxury so we burned wood, sawdust, or whatever was available. Sometimes we would have to open the windows and doors to let the smoke out. Of course the wind would freeze us and we would be back to square one and with our attire, we were far from being well equipped. Clothing was also a problem.

One could not find cloth. I was fortunate that my mother was a resourceful seamstress and made some jackets and coats out of old ones. She also managed to get me another pair of shoes since the only pair I had were deteriorated beyond repair. Somehow my mother had managed to get me a pair of shoes with wooden soles but with real leather tops (at this time leather was a luxury item). These shoes were a lifesaver in that at least they were closed; the others were merely sandals with rubber soles.

The Blue Ring

Attending The Schools in "Marignane"

Meanwhile school was held on a regular basis. The hours had changed due to so many interruptions from "air raids". As previously mentioned, we attended school from 8:00 a.m. until 6:00 p.m. with a short break for lunch and to allow for the unpredictable air raids. Vacations were a thing of the past. School was in attendance summer and winter.

The English language and another foreign language of our choice were required by the school system. These rules were in effect until the Germans moved in. Then our school sessions were often interrupted when the Germans invaded our classrooms by storming in unannounced. They would question our teachers on the lessons being taught, strongly enforcing that the students learn German instead of English. According to them, German was going to become the International Language instead of English.

I was the leader of my class as well as President of the Honor Society and Students Organization and because of this I was questioned by the Germans as to which languages I was studying. To their disappointment, they found that I was not learning German as was strongly suggested, but English and Italian. The Germans continued to harass our classes for weeks on end, scaring everyone more and more. As this persisted, not only the students but the teachers as well, decided it was not worth the pains to go against the Germans' wishes. English was dropped and German became the main foreign language studied. I abhorred the thought of taking German but I continued to learn Italian. Since Italian was also classified as an enemy language like German, I got away with refusing to learn German. Later I regretted not having taken German because I would have been able to be of more help with the FFI. I was, however, determined to continue learning English. Somehow I knew I would find a way to learn it on my own.

The "Cours Mirabeau," an extremely large avenue was located at the center of the town of *Marignane*. The entire length of this avenue had a traffic island in the middle. The beginning was more like a park with benches under acacia trees which provided shade. Older people often came here to watch the children play. Along this avenue there was the monument dedicated to World War I with the names of the soldiers who had lost their lives. On the other side of the monument was a large asphalt area where there were open markets set up on certain days of the week. These markets were like a swap meet where produce as well as clothing and sundries were being sold during peace time. On the right side of the avenue there were stores, bars, lounges, and night-clubs; also a very large building which was the City Hall and was parallel with the World War I monument, L'Hotêl Moderne and more shops. On the left side of the avenue there were more large buildings which were medical offices, followed by a very impressive mansion, several two-storied homes next to the garden of this mansion and then a small cul-de-sac which led to the school buildings in the background. On the opposite of this access way was the post office, a small shop, an office supply store, followed by another hotel and finally a few small villas with gardens in front.

The mansion which was previously mentioned, was owned by the "Terras" family now with the three sisters remaining. These sisters were Ernestine who was an old maid, Eoline who was a divorcee, and Geraldine who was a widow. These three very nice ladies who lived together were highly respected in the community. Ernestine taught shorthand, typing and accounting. Eoline supposedly helped Ernestine and Geraldine was a music teacher.

When the Germans occupied the city, they moved in on the rez-de-chausses (the ground level) of the Terras' mansion and made it their central headquarters. Surprisingly enough, they allowed the three sisters to continue living in the rooms on the top floor, permitting them to continue their profession of teaching privately.

At this time, our school system had been entirely turned upside down. Our Lycée consisted of junior high school, high school and college studies combined. There were no ball games, sports, marching bands, socializing, dances, or gatherings. In fact anytime a group of students tried to talk to one another, we had to disband since no more than three people were allowed to talk together. Typing, shorthand and accounting, as well as music and the fine arts were not considered basic subjects. Therefore, these subjects had to be taken privately.

This is why I ended up going to the Terras' mansion to attend evening classes three nights out of the week at 7:00 p.m. There were no words to describe the continual fear I had going to the Terras' mansion. My mother worried about this constantly and she had a good reason to be concerned since at that time I was an adolescent. This was in 1941 and it went on for several years. I was issued a second pass of identification with my picture which allowed me to pass the sentries at the mansion's entrance and go to the upstairs rooms where the private classes were held. I had to constantly watch what I said and to whom I was talking. During some of the classes I attended at the Terras' I was the only student. Other times there would be one or two other students (never more than three) attending.

The three sisters each had a bedroom upstairs, however, since they were almost entirely confined to the rooms upstairs, they were often in the library which was used as our schoolroom. While we were taking Ernestine's classes, it was not unusual to have Eoline and Geraldine remaining in the library even though they had no real reason for being there except maybe from sheer boredom. The Germans frequently would stomp up the stairs to the library, looking over our shoulders, while the teachers would put on this great act pretending to be deeply involved.

Eoline was Ernestine's assistant but it seemed that her duties were of a different kind. Not letting anyone know she spoke German she would stand guard during the lessons, anticipating the Germans when they would storm into our classroom unannounced. Actually it seemed that during our classes, both sisters, Eoline and Geraldine, spent most of their time listening by the door. Moreover, these three ladies were very plain and did nothing to make themselves attractive.

Ernestine was a dear lady but she was so upset about the Germans downstairs that she barely dared to breathe. She also was constantly shaking. The other students and I could always tell the time by the color of her face. At first her face would turn pink, by the middle of class the pink in her face would extend to the top of her ears. The students and I would glance at each other while doing our work and would have a hard time holding our giggles. We knew without looking at the clock that as soon as her face and ears were beet red that the class would be dismissed.

Occasionally the Germans would burst in to see if we were plotting. They had no trust in us. Many times I saw the sisters listening with their heads near the door or to the floor. To this day I don't know if they were part of the Resistance. Eoline would ask me a lot of questions, some of which were extremely ridiculous. I could not tell if they were working for the FFI, however, the questions bothered me. I was usually instructed to ask my uncles these questions and they in turn would give me ridiculous "childish" answers that I was told to give to the instructors. A few examples of these ludicrous questions were: Did my Uncle Pipo do housework? Had he ever helped his wife clean house? Could he cook? How about my Uncle Lino? Did he play any musical instruments? My uncles' questions to the instructors were no better. They would ask questions like: Did my teachers like to hike? Did they prefer wheels like a bike? I really thought that if these questions had no double meaning, then they all were losing their minds. The funny thing about it was they were not even acquainted.

Still determined to take English I finally convinced Mr. Pereau, one of my teachers at the Lycée that I attended everyday, to instruct me privately. So began my secret escapades to Mr. Pereau's home to study English on the nights that I wouldn't go to the Terras' for classes. I would use my two badges to pass security, then I would go to my English class. I would never know when class would be held until the last minute because Mr. Pereau was extremely cautious and fearful of being caught. It was inevitably a last minute notice on my way out of school. Mr. Pereau would merely give me a signal such as a nod of the head which indicated that he would give me my English class that night. I was terribly worried myself, fearing the strong chances of my being caught, yet I was compelled to learn no matter what it entailed. I often wondered how could I explain that I was learning English at night privately because the Germans had completely prohibited it to be taught in our regular school. My mother also constantly worried about me and my safety. I really don't know how she coped now that I look back.

I was very tall for my age and as I grew older my mother began being obsessed with the way I dressed. She concentrated on making me look awful.

My hair was long and untidy and I wore no makeup of any kind. I remember looking into the mirror and giving my stringy hair a hopeless tussle. After my mother saw me doing this she had tried to console me by telling me how beautiful I was. She then warned me that the Germans loved beautiful girls and that they did bad things to them. I remember her saying, "As long as you know that you are beautiful and I know that you are beautiful, that is enough." At that time, however, I was far from being convinced that this was true. While I was hugging my mother, I can still visualize myself looking over my mother's shoulder at my reflection in the mirror and sticking my tongue out at my plain image.

When I first came to stay in *Marignane*, she had made me some beautiful clothes with remnants from some of her old dresses and dresses that she had sewn for her various clientele. According to her, however, they were too nice. I had to look worse so that the Germans would not give me a second look. She managed to find an old military blanket which was a sickening shade of greenish yellow and made me an awful coat. I just dreaded wearing this coat. I felt like a poor peasant and I always became sick to my stomach when I had to wear it. My mother had given me the choice - either wear it or freeze to death. So I wore it with no other alternative. I did not realize until later that my mother really saved my life. Dressing down was for my own good and was the best protection I had from being harmed or killed by the Germans.

My Involvement With "La Resistance"

When the Germans first occupied France, all of the French people were required to report to the main German headquarters. Everyone was interrogated, registered and then assigned passes depending on where they lived. As a result of reporting to the German authorities, many arrests were made for no particular reason. This was most likely due to the increased amount of reports that were given to the German authorities or merely because the Germans needed manpower. Because of this, mostly young men were arrested and then sent to labor camps.

Since both of my uncles were natives of Italy, even though they were French citizens, they were both arrested. One day, German trucks came to their shop, helped themselves to their machinery including their motorcycles and arrested both of them. My two uncles were then taken to a bigger headquarters in *Marseille*, right in front of *La Gare St. Charles*, the main railroad station where all the trains loaded prisoners that were headed for Germany's labor camps. My entire family was devastated.

My mother, who was well known and considered blue blood by marriage, had many friends and didn't hesitate to have them interfere on behalf of her brothers. The Prefet (similar to governor) came to the rescue. After three or four days of endless deliberations and many promises, both of my uncles were released on one condition: they were to work for the Germans in their shop for free and should consider themselves "under house arrest". This meant that they were not allowed to leave the shop nor their house which was attached. If they were to leave the premises at any time and be caught, they would not have a second chance. They would be authorized to work for others for money since they needed to support their family but everyone coming to the shop was going to be investigated and no more than two people at a time were allowed to be in the shop. Therefore my mother and I thought that the best thing for us to do was to move into my oldest Uncle Pipo's villa next to his shop. Here we could help my two uncles continue to live a somewhat normal life.

Moving in and living with my Uncle Pipo had its pros and cons. I had to go to the headquarters to have my picture taken, answer a lot of questions and obtain a pass so that the Germans could authorize me to live with my uncles. I was terrified. To this day I can still smell that awful odor of unwashed uniforms and cigarette smoke. To make matters even worse, my Uncle Pipo's villa was closer to the airport which was a likely target for bombing. Fortunately we had our own shelter which was only a few feet from the front door of the villa. We no longer had to run to the nearest community air raid shelter.

According to the rumors, a lot of activity was taking place at the airport. All flights had long since been canceled when the Germans occupied France.

The employees, however, had been allowed to go in and out of the airport to maintain the commercial aircrafts. This no longer was the case. There were not any aircrafts left and no employees were allowed in or out unless they were employed by the Germans and if this were the case, you could not trust them. Several checkpoints were in place at various entrances of the airport. There were sentries everywhere and it was believed that some of the fields surrounding the hangars were mined.

The "Boulevard du Nord" was the shortest and most direct way to the airport from *Marignane*. At the end of the "Boulevard du Nord" there was a checkpoint with two sentries on guard around-the-clock. At that point the boulevard ended and became two roads, both directed to the airport creating a V shape. The road on the left was called "Route de l'Aviation" which led to my Uncle Pipo's shop approximately one-half mile from the checkpoint. The other road was called "Route du Cimetiere" because it passed right in front of the cemetery. From my uncle's shop one could see the activity on both of these roads. Some of the FFI had at first cautiously approached my two uncles, Pipo and Lino. Their main purpose was to have them watch the activities on these roads and alert and inform them of any peculiar happenings. The shop was in an ideal location for this. My mother, my aunt and myself, however, were oblivious and unaware of both my uncles' involvement with the FFI. While they worked in their shop, they secretly kept track of all the equipment on the convoys that frequently traversed to-and-from the airport on both of these roads. Even the tiniest details were taken into account. Before my two uncles were placed under "house arrest" they had taken turns delivering their information into the proper hands. After they were arrested and then released (which we later thought was caused by someone who turned them in), my uncles found themselves in a very precarious position. Therefore, some members of the "Réseau" began coming to their shop under the pretense of having some work done and would get the information from my uncles as well as deliver instruction to them. For security purposes, all that the "Réseau" members knew were where to deliver their information and when, just like my uncles had known where to pass on the communication they received or saw. This was very risky and all precautions had to be taken. Another plan had to be taken to protect our family and all that were involved.

Finally after a long time of contemplating, my uncles decided that one of us should deliver the information. The first person that came to mind was my mother, but that was out of the question. She had intervened for my uncles' release and some of the civilians whose relatives had not been so lucky, were extremely resentful. Blue blood or not, they would not hesitate to turn us all in. The next family member considered was my Aunt Yvonne, Uncle Pipo's wife. She went to the stores to do her marketing and this made her have easy access to all of the people who were able to lead a somewhat normal life. Most of these people were heavily involved with the "Réseau", later known as the FFI. At this time, however, my Aunt Yvonne and Uncle Pipo had three little boys they were raising. The youngest was René, who was still being nursed by

Yvonne, the second was Claude who was not quite three years old, and the eldest was Jean (nicknamed Jeannot) who was five years old. The consequences of my Aunt Yvonne being caught would be devastating and would jeopardize the entire family's safety. All seemed lost.

Then my Uncle Pipo had an absurd yet possible idea. There was little-old-me who had a pass with my identification and picture which allowed me to go to school and to stand in line for food at the Pilia's store. I could cross the checkpoint at *Boulevard du Nord* easily and did it everyday. Being so young, looking so innocent and scared worked in my favor and being in the dark would protect me. No one would suspect me being involved with the FFI. As expected, my pass did not allow me to go and cross during curfew hours. Therefore I became the most likely one to follow my two uncles' footsteps. The telephone had been disconnected by the Germans. No one, however, would take a chance with public communication anyway. One never knew who was listening. My uncles kept me entirely oblivious to the information I was helping them transmit. Moreover, they didn't mention my involvement to Yvonne or my mother. The less anyone knew, the better. They decided to have me deliver whatever information was needed to inform the involved parties. This information was cleverly hidden within certain materials such as food, tools or other everyday necessities. Their perfectly strategic plan would have to protect me as well.

Roger (I never knew his last name) had a butcher shop near the apartment we used to rent. He frequently had the shop closed rather than open due to the fact that there was only one distribution of meat per month. He had, however, made many contacts in the shop so he decided to keep it open with the excuse to remodel it. Due to the fact that he was not very good at carpentry and never came to our shop, he wrote my two uncles who in turn drafted some blueprints with their ideas on the construction. I was the one who delivered these blueprints to Roger.

Then I was asked to deliver various hardware supplies such as screws and nails that my uncles had in their shop since there were no hardware stores and no other way for Roger to obtain these supplies. At the various checkpoints, the Germans would search my packages and then allow me to go through; all they found was the miscellaneous hardware supplies I had to deliver. As these deliveries continued, the Germans grew tired of checking my packages of hardware and began to just allow me go through with a mere nod of their heads. Unknown to the Germans, my innocent deliveries were extremely important to my uncles and everyone involved with *La Resistance*. Every time that I crossed the *Boulevard du Nord* checkpoint my uncles wanted to know all of the details. This included how the Germans would search my packages, the questions they asked when I was being interrogated, the surroundings and any unusual happenings. Like so many others involved in *La Resistance*, this is how I innocently started to become a carrier.

Many times I would take Roger some special screws and nails for a particular job and he would disappear to the back of his shop. Then he would usually return some of them, telling me that they didn't fit. I would then return home with the unused hardware and deliver his message. My uncle would then scratch his head and would give me something else to deliver. Moreover, he would often tell me to go to the baker and see if by chance he had the type of hardware that Roger needed. After many trips, which I had to do on foot since I was not big enough to ride my uncles' bicycles, I began to find these deliveries ridiculous. I couldn't understand why Roger wouldn't go to the other store himself since it was just around the corner from him. Later, I realized that Roger never went out so as not to arouse any suspicion with the ones with whom he collaborated.

Nonetheless, I continued these deliveries on quite a regular basis. I can remember that more blueprints were roughly prepared by my Uncle Pipo. Obviously they were hard to understand because I had to go back to Roger with the same drawings. Every time I brought them back, however, Pipo would add some figures or slightly change the drawings. Much later I learned that Roger was their contact and the figures somehow indicated the activity to and from the airport on both roads: *Route de l'Aviation* and *Route du Cimetiere*. Even the hardware had a meaning, a code of some kind. At that time I did not know what was going on. Nonetheless, I remember shuddering every time I crossed the German checkpoint with their bayonets surrounding me. This state of affairs lasted for almost two years. I had no idea how valuable I had become.

In the meantime, the BBC was keeping our hopes alive. It would bring us words of encouragement and then a lot of coded messages which sounded like of lot of nonsense such as "Marie's soup was not warm" or "The pie was ready", "The coffee pot was boiling over", etc. These messages were meaningless to us yet we enjoyed listening to them. Somehow they were words that proved to us that something was happening and it gave us hope and encouragement we so desperately needed. Often we would enjoy trying to guess what the true meaning was behind all of their nonsensical sayings. For instance "The pie was ready" could mean they were ready to land or "The soup was not warm" could be a warning to someone to hold some operation.

The Germans of course had prohibited for anyone to listen to the BBC. It was directly under the supervision of the S.S. (the most vicious) who would storm in unannounced, smash the radio down and take the head of the family to headquarters for endless interrogations, keep them, and eventually ship him or her to Germany, to the camps. Rumors were that some of the people cought could be accused of spying and therefore be shot.

I can remember that when the broadcast started, the introduction was a sound of three gongs. They were so penetrating that you could hear it over all the outside noises and through the walls. It could actually make the hair stand up on the back of one's head, however, it filled you with hope and excitement. We knew the danger of being on the BBC wave lenght, but we needed hope, and we knew that someone out there was working towards freedom, trying to reach out to us.

My Involvement with the Resistance

I expect it would be like someone who had been trapped in a cave for some-time and suddenly hearing the sounds of the rescue team.

To protect my family we had various signals that we used to warn the listeners of impending danger from the Germans. Usually I was to stand watch on the "veranda". Vines surrounded this porch from top to bottom which made it an enclosed area. The table and chairs were conveniently placed near the front door of the villa. My uncle's dog was by my side. (As long as I could remember, my uncle always had a dog.) The present large dog, Tudor, was getting old. Although Tudor occasionally roamed around the courtyard he had very little ambition, spending most of his time in the doghouse. My uncle had given me a whistle that only a dog could hear and that would start Tudor barking which in turn got the other dogs in the vicinity joining in. This was one of the signals that helped my family know that the Germans were in the vicinity and were doing their search rounds. However, we did not use this signal unless we were sure the Germans did not have their dogs.

One signal that our family often used was using the water pump. Our supply of water came from a well located between the house and the shelter. We had a pump inside that we handled manually and another outside which we did not use very often. This pump, for lack of use, became very rusty, squeaking a lot. I always left a bucket there so that I would pretend to be getting some water. All signals had to be perceived as very innocent.

Another warning that we frequently used was very subtle and quiet. This was the use of an extension cord which was located under the table. My uncle had managed to get a rudimentary plug on a side of the veranda. The extension cord was connected to a lamp at the back of the house, close to where the radio was located. This lamp could not conveniently be seen from the front of the house since our windows were tinted blue according to the "Black out Law". If the lamp came on, one of my uncles would immediately turn if off along with the radio and everyone would scatter around the house picking up some kind of task which had all been preplanned and thought out ahead of time. Everyone was so well rehearsed that every action they took looked very natural and innocent. Moreover, the volume of the radio was never high since our family was always huddled around the radio. The only real giveaway was the sound of the gong.

The other two signals were less ingenious. A chime was hanging from the front eaves of the roof which was covered by the climbing vines that enclosed the veranda. The cats loved to lay there during the day. So I used the cats, pretending that they started the chime or maybe hit some aluminum dish on the table.

We definitely had a problem since my two uncles were put on house arrest. The Germans would pop in and out of the shop unannounced for small jobs or merely just to check on us. I believe at some point our neighbors may have thought we were friendly with the Germans since they were visiting our home so frequently. We did not dare to confide in anyone. Everyone believed what they wanted. Our family's main concern was to survive; nothing else really mattered. The agreement that was made between my two uncles and the Germans through 'the Prefet" was that they would work for the Germans for free. And that is what they did.

Our home life was a nightmare. We were always living life on the edge. Constantly anxious, suspicious and mostly terrified yet we never would admit it. Even the children felt the tension, they were cranky and unhappy. I can just picture my short and robust aunt, Yvonne. She had the most expressive face with her long, beautiful dark hair and dark brown eyes. If my Uncle Pipo was acting like 'life was just a bowl of cherries', my aunt would just roll her eyes in the most comical way and would tell him, "Tell me how great life is when the Germans come and…" without finishing her sentence, she would gesture with her hand as if she was cutting her throat. My uncle would always laugh but you could feel the seriousness in the room and one could cut the uneasiness and tension with a knife

One day Uncle Pipo asked if I would like to ride his bike. I told him, "I'd love to, but it still may be too big for me to ride." I remember him just shrugging his shoulders and saying, "We won't know until we try." So after a few trial runs of riding the bike on the road to see how I could handle it and a few minor adjustments including lowering the seat, I was able to ride my uncle's bike. I was so thrilled! The next day he asked if I wanted to do an errand for him on the bicycle and naturally I was ecstatic. I was to ride towards the airport. A couple hundred feet from the entrance of the airport lived an old man in a rundown shack where he raised chickens. Sometimes he would walk by my uncle's shop on his way to town. My uncle, however, had not seen him for a very long time and was beginning to worry so he wanted me to go and check on him and see how he was doing. If someone stopped me, I was to show them the money my uncle gave me and tell them I was getting eggs for his children. My uncle also gave me a bag made of cloth for bringing back the eggs. As I was leaving for the airport I remember him saying, "Tell them one of the kids is sick. It usually works."

It was a beautiful day and to my surprise and relief, no one stopped me. I did not encounter a single German. I had no problem finding the shack. So I came off the bike and called out, "Is anyone here?" but no one answered. I was about to turn around when suddenly a man came from behind the bushes. I didn't know his name and I actually had never met him before. I told him that my uncle had sent me to see if he was alright and also to get some eggs. (I did not, however, see or hear any chickens nearby.) With a very guarded look, he asked me a few questions as to establish my identity and then told me to follow him inside. He asked me if I had met anyone on my way to his place and when I told him, "No," he seemed to relax. His eyes, however, never stopped moving, constantly looking toward the door and back. Finally he went to a corner of the room, picked up two eggs and wrapped them in paper. All the time he was talking very low key about the action going on day and night at the refinery in *Berre*.

L'etang de Berre was the body of water that was connected to the sea. It was enclosed like a harbor. The airport was located on the very right of us and about midway to the estuary was the town of *Berre*. The refinery was next to this town, constantly in full action and smoking up a storm. Barges were able to come up through the estuary from the sea, load up the fuel, and leave the same way. This was not a regular way to come in, but was actually reserved for landing and taking off of the planes, which at this time were strictly for the Germans.

I could see lots of military trucks next to the refinery as well as a couple of flat boats. The man kept on talking and said that he hoped someone would come to bomb them before they took all of the gasoline from the tanks. He continued to mumble and told me to wait until he came back. (He must have gone to check if there were any Germans on the road.) Soon he returned and warned me to be careful as I was going home. I then left with the eggs and fortunately didn't run into any problems. Actually it was really strange, not a soul.

Once home, my uncle wanted me to repeat word per word what the old man had said. He also wanted to know if I asked for two eggs or if he decided himself the amount. It all seemed so very strange to me and at that moment it occurred to me that I never paid for the eggs. I gave the money back to my uncle and he seemed just as perplexed as I was. At that point the same reoccuring thought came to me! Something was going on but I was always kept in the dark. Why?!

Two days later, in the early hours of the morning, the Allies bombed the airport and the refinery in *Berre*. It was one of the worst air raids in the history of *Marignane*. High in the sky we could see the flames in the flurry of activity; the aim had been perfect. The 'petrol' burned for days. The refinery was no more.

That event sent me into deep thought. I started to recall all of the things I had done during the previous days including my trip to the old man near the airport. It also occurred to me that I had delivered a bill to the bakery a few doors down from Roger on my way to school. Coincidence?! As the war escalated, so did my errands, "commissions" as they called them. (At the time they seemed like assignments to me.) I still did not realize the impact of all of these events, however I was becoming very suspicious. Now and then some remarks were made but no one ever really told the real truth point blank.

Air raids increased and became, once again, a normal occurrence. Since the Germans were more in a state of alarm, they started to act less obnoxious and perturbed toward us. All day in school rumors had circulated that something was going on at the airport. At least there was a lot of activity going on there. The Germans had brought trucks of soldiers and everyone was working on special projects.

I had made a point to go home at noon and walked in the house. Not being expected so early, I found my two uncles bent over a map that was very roughly drawn. They were so intense that they jumped when I addressed them.

Immediately they pretended to talk about their woodwork as if they were planning to build some kind of intricate cabinetry that required the attention of both of them. "What are you doing home?" questioned my Uncle Lino as he was trying to cover up what I was beginning to be aware of concerning their activities. I nonchalantly answered, "I forgot something for my class this afternoon." While I was acting as if I was searching for something, I began to talk to them casually yet I could not hide my overwhelming curiosity. "The school seems to be very upset with all of the rumors circulating about the truck loads of soldiers that were being taken to the airport to finish some construction project," I stated. "Actually," I added, "the Germans are so preoccupied that at the usual checkpoints they did not even acknowledge me and this is very rare." I noticed the exchange of looks between them. Uncle Pipo asked, "Where did the truck loads of soldiers come from? We have not seen any activity on the roads around here." "Perhaps some other direction, like from Berre. In fact one of my schoolmates, Denise, told me this but I can't believe her because she is always coming up with stories," I immediately responded, noticing their suspicious looks.

That night before I went to bed I prepared all of my stuff for the air raids as usual, then my school books and I went into the large kitchen where my mother and my aunt were sitting and talking. The kids were in bed and there was no sign of my uncles; that was unusual. My aunt mentioned that they had a rather urgent job and were in the shop working. I went to the veranda and could not see any light which was not peculiar since these were the rules for "blackout". So after bidding everyone a good night, I called it a day.

The next day Denise was in the middle of a group gossiping when suddenly the Germans came in. Needless to say, this put an end to whatever she was going to report. After school I went home and noticed the restlessness of the Germans. After a meager meal, I returned to town to attend my class that was at the home of Mademoiselle Terras. Ironically, there was only one sentry at the checkpoint and he was on the phone, so I proceeded. Moreover, I was surprised to find that I was the only student attending class. Eoline said she had talked to the mothers of two of the students and they both were ill. This was very suspicious since I had just seen both of these students attending school earlier that morning. It seemed very coincidental that they both got ill that same afternoon. Nonetheless, my teachers and I went to the library to start our lessons as usual. The three ladies were extremely nervous and restless. I had only been there thirty minutes when Ernestine suddenly looked sharply at Eoline, who after a moment of hesitation exclaimed, "We are cutting this class short. I suggest that you immediately go straight home! *Pas de questions, s'il vous plaît!*" (No questions please!) Intrigued but not worried, I left and went straight home as was advised.

That same night, I had been sleeping in a very deep state when I was awakened by the blaring siren announcing the air raid. As I had done so many times, I thanked God that the shelter was so close to the house. I could hear the "mitrailleuses" (machine guns) blasting at full speed. This was a bad one since the siren had barely gone off when the firing had started. Explosions were resounding everywhere. When this type of "alert" happened, I could understand how people would get so disorientated and could so easily head straight into the line of fire because the shooting was all around us and there was no place to be safe. It had almost a paralyzing effect because of the extreme terror we were up against.

Partly blinded by the light of the blaze, we crossed from the villa to the shelter. My Aunt Yvonne was carrying the baby Réne who was still fast asleep while my two uncles grabbed the other two who were very frightened. My mother and I being last in line, carried the usual necessary supplies that were not left in the shelter at all times. We were barely under cover when the actual bombing started. It seemed like it was right outside. The ground shook as if we were experiencing an earthquake and the shelling was occurring right above our heads! The children were crying so we tried to calm them down as much as possible and we kept quiet sitting on the benches with a stick of wood in our mouths. This was to prevent our lungs from exploding in case of impact.

We had no idea how long we sat there, perhaps one or two hours. We were all too stunned and terrified to really care. Much later, when the explosions subsided and after the siren had announced the "all clear" signal, the adults left the shelter and went to investigate if it was safe to bring the children out. So I remained with the kids until one of the adults would come and tell me it was safe and we would all head for bed. This was a normal ritual.

There I sat, numb and empty of thoughts for what seemed like forever. The children had already fallen asleep and I felt like I was half asleep myself, when a voice coming from the top of the stairs whispered, "Marie-Jeanne? Are you asleep?" Then shortly after this, Uncle Pipo appeared, his face ashen. He was shaking me lightly, "Marie-Jeanne," he said, "Run and go fetch Doctor Brocheré." "Who is ill?" I asked. He answered, "Your mother." Immediately I wanted to see her, but he insisted that there was no time for this and that I should "Go and run fast". She had to be terribly sick and it must have suddenly happened. So overwhelmed by emotion, I felt like my heart was going to explode.

Panic set in, I ran all of the way to the checkpoint, tears running down my face, praying and whispering under my breath, "Please God, don't let anything happen to her!" At the checkpoint, an incredible confusion was taking place. Unlike what normally took place, (being stopped by the Germans holding bayonets,) the Germans were shouting, trucks were running in all directions, and the telephones were ringing. I tried to get the sentries attention. I was hysterical. I was not wearing my badge. Instead I had grabbed it from my uncle's hand and had stuck it in my pocket. I told the Germans that I needed a doctor. They seemed to understand doctor and I pointed down the Boulevard du Nord towards the residence of the doctor. Then they pointed to my lapel and I pulled my pass from my pocket. They were confused about all of the commotion that was taking place. For a short time I didn't know if I was going to be able to save my mother. Getting the doctor meant everything to me. Finally they let me cross and continued to watch me from a distance, ringing the doctor's bell. Then in minutes both of us were running back. The doctor was trying to finish dressing. We did not stop at the checkpoint on the way back and the Germans didn't try to stop us. I burst into the house and went directly to the bedroom. No one was there. I retraced my steps and went back to the kitchen. There, around a large table sat my mother, my aunt and my two uncles who were ashen, and had their mouths open. The kids must have been in bed. A sense of relief washed over me, immediately followed by anger towards my uncle. Yet as I stared at their grim faces I realized we were in trouble. A different kind of trouble. At that very moment all I learned from Nini, all I had heard and experienced, listening to both my father and my brother came to me and the word "WARNING" was not just in my mind. All of a sudden I believe I grew up, 13 years old going on 40.

I took charge of the situation. I ordered my mother to undress and get into bed immediately! Then I led Dr. Broché with his case into the bedroom following my mother and told the bewildered doctor to look professional. As for the rest of the family, they were so startled by my actions that they didn't have to pretend. I told them, "The Germans were right behind me so act accordingly. They will be here in five minutes." We heard the knock on the door within two minutes. I opened the door immediately since the Germans knew I had fetched the doctor. However, these Germans were not the ones I expected. These were the SS, the most vicious ones. They ordered everyone outside and were going to search the house. Uncle Pipo and I took charge and asked them to follow us into the children's bedroom. All of the rest of the family went outside. The Germans then saw my mother in bed being cared for by Dr. Broché and walked out. Once outside they pointed at the shop, so again Pipo and I entered the shop where we showed them the entire area. After the Germans had taken most of the machinery, it looked more like a hangar. At the back of the shop there was an area used for wood shavings, sawdust and all kinds of wood cuttings large and small. After looking around and lifting some pieces of wood and dropping them back down again, they prodded with their bayonets. Satisfied, we assumed, they left. The Germans were definitely on a search party. After making sure the SS were on their way to another house, Pipo and I went inside. The doctor was no longer in the bedroom. As soon as the Germans had left, he was directed to the pile of junk in the back of the shop through a back door by my Uncle Lino.

Then finally the truth came out. A bomber plane had crashed in the field across from the shop. This must have been the loud explosion I had heard over our heads just a few hours before. The British pilot had gotten away from the plane but was severely wounded. He had managed to crawl out of the field and attract the attention of my family when they left the shelter. My family had doctored him as much as they could, then carried him into the junk yard where they hid him under a bunch of wood shavings so he could be safe from detection. My uncles had taken a large door, put it on a small support and slid the pilot under this, fearing that the Germans may just do what they did - prod the pile.

My Involvement with the Resistance

That night no one slept. I was assigned to keep watch outside on the veranda with a blanket wrapped around me. I was reminded of the signals while my two uncles, the doctor, and the rest of the family were busy with the pilot whom I never saw. While I sat outside on guard, I tried to cool down my anger towards my Uncle Pipo. I felt he hadn't trusted me to keep a secret and I was extremely resentful. As the hours passed, however, I realized that he and my entire family were trying to protect me. I relived all of the experiences of the past years since my uncles' house arrests and I understood—they had no choice.

The doctor came back several times, to check on my mother who was supposed to be ill for several days. She could not go anywhere, not even outside for fear to be caught. After a few days the pilot's condition improved. Now the only problem was to get him out of the country. I was not included on this venture. Nevertheless, I could judge the progress by feeling the tension around me. I had to stay outside and be on guard most of the time while everyone was listening to the BBC.

After four days that seemed like four years, I came home from school to find my family looking almost normal again. The pilot had been picked up! My Uncle Pipo expressed extreme relief by sighing and saying, "We made it!" All of the messages from the BBC had been relayed to the pilot and one of these messages must have given instructions of where and when he was to be picked up. From that moment on, I was definitely aware of my previous actual "activities" and the danger we were all facing. I had just grown up overnight, the hard way. The lines of communication began to open between my uncles and myself; they had finally decided to share their knowledge with me.

I learned that France had built a very special plane, known as a "Prototype". This plane was supposed to achieve a series of records in flying, bombing, speed, detection, among other features. According to rumors, it had been kept at one of Paris' airports, *Le Bourget*. When the Germans occupied northern France, they of course, took charge of the plane. They tried to get the blueprints and other information on it. The French, however, claimed that during the air raids the Germans had destroyed these records. The Germans decided then to take it apart and learn what made this prototype so special. They needed a place where the Allies would not find it. The *Marseille/Marignane* Airport was the Germans' solution. What a better place than the south of France which was supposed to be unoccupied at this time?!

The Germans proceeded to build a large hangar. A good part of this was in the ground so that the building would match the other hangars. When the special storage was terminated after weeks of excavating and completed with a special roof, a convoy brought the dismantled plane to the airport in the middle of the night. At all times it was guarded by security and unfortunately, the FFI couldn't do a thing about it. There had been some failing attempts by them to blow it up and the results were severe retaliation by the Germans with increased security and many arrests. Exactly ten days later, the

Germans had completed the assemblage of the plane. This is when the terrible bombing occurred. The new hangar and the plane had been pulverized. In fact, the entire airport had become useless with the runways full of excavations like an aftermath earthquake. There was no other choice but for the Germans to close the airport. Sadly enough there had been many lives taken and some homes around the airport and their occupants had vanished. The pilot that my uncles had helped was part of the bombardment group. He had dropped his bomb and was on his way out when unfortunately he was shot down. Someone had warned the Allies about the plane.

I thought about Eoline, living above the German headquarters, understanding their language, sending me home early. Did she know? She probably told the mothers of the other two students not to come. She could not tell me because she didn't live in my area and therefore she had no pass for the checkpoint on the Boulevard du Nord. Could it have been her? Then I thought of the old man I had gone to see. The man who had given me the two eggs and talking about the refinery and two days later, the refinery was no more. A shiver came over me. I realized how many people were involved against the fight of the Germans. Then I thought of how my family was involved with my two uncles under house arrest. I could not forget that if they were caught, there would be no mercy. What a nightmare.

. . .

With the knowledge of my actual role in the Underground, I became aware of the happenings around me. This was not a game, this was real. I was not delivering hardware, I was carrying coded messages, drawings with numbers reporting movements of equipment and troups. My guesses were now a reality.

Among many of the endless situations we ran into, one was to try to help people that for one reason or another were in serious trouble.

One night, returning from my class at Mademoiselle Terras I had just crossed the checkpoint, where along the road some homes were located. About halfway between the checkpoint and our home there was a very large villa which the Germans had requisitioned and it was rumored some officers lived there. The villa was surrounded with a high iron fence and big trees, partly concealing the house. There was a good-sized courtyard between the house and the gate. It was occupied by all kinds of military vehicles, including motorcycles with sidecars. Across from this property were hangar-type buildings somewhat dilapidated, high trees and vines mixed with wild bushes. Everytime I went home I had to pass this house and I did so on the other side of the road, as far away from sight as possible. It was beginning to rain and I walked briskly trying to blend into the darkness. As I reached the beginning of the property, unable to see the house through the trees, I heard a terrible scream, followed by another and yet another from the same direction. It was so loud that it chilled my blood. I stopped immediately and withdrew in the bushes. I had no idea what to do; it sounded like a girl in trouble. My first thought was I am in real danger myself. There is absolutely nothing I can do. I was rooted to the ground. I felt petrified with fear. It had been rumored that Germans had held orgies over here but these screams were not from someone participating in an orgy, but by a victim held against her will. I knew I could do nothing except get home safely and report the incident. Our house was just around the bend. Maybe my family could think of something. As I started to leave, a couple of German soldiers came out of the house into the courtyard and looked around, laughing. I retreated back into the darkness and waited until they finally went back inside. Then I ran home.

I rushed into the house, extremely upset and went directly to the kitchen where I found my two uncles, my mother and my aunt all waiting for my return from school, as usual. They never went to bed until I was home safely. Immediately alarmed, they stared at me while I told them what I had just witnessed.

All five of us debated what to do, with no solution. By that time it was a little past 9:00 p.m. The curfew would begin at 11:00 p.m., so whatever we were going to do had to be done now. We hoped that the girl would be able to escape. Who knew what the Germans, once finished with her, would decide to do with her. We finally agreed that Lino and Pipo would go into the shop, open a window, wait in the dark, and keep an eye on the road. I would head back toward town, appearing as though I had to go for a doctor. My mother did not like the idea at all. She knew it was hopeless and would put me in danger. I assured her that I would not do a thing to get in trouble. I would only look.

I carefully turned onto the dirt road and looked, but did nothing except hold my breath and stay out of sight. I arrived from the opposite direction and before I even reached the dirt road I heard shouts all around. As I got closer I saw Germans running around their vehicles. I quickly ran down the dirt road leading away from the property. I knew there was nothing I could do except be careful and return home without being seen. Bordering the dirt road were trees and some kind of a field with high overgrown weeds. I decided to take that way around and disappear into the neglected field. After some time had passed, while I was trying to get back to the shop, I saw something that looked like a bunch of rags, half-hidden. I walked cautiously in that direction and realized it was a girl lying in a fetal position, shivering. I crawled in her direction and whispered "Don't move, I am a friend." When I got closer I saw she was in shock. Her clothes were torn; she was bleeding on her forehead, had blood on her neck, and from what I could see also on her chest. I tried to figure out what to do next, so I asked, "Are you hurt?" She just stared, trembling, so I gave her my jacket and repeated the question, asking her to answer yes or no by shaking her head. Could she walk or crawl? She nodded yes. So I added, "I do not live far from here, but we have to take the long way around to avoid being seen." Again she nodded her head. I said, "The most important thing is to get out of here. Follow me."

We started crawling, stopping every so often to give her a chance to rest and I would ask, "Ça va?" (Are you okay?) She would nod but I could see we were going too slow and she was getting worse. I wanted to get her to our house, but it was more important to get her away from the Germans. We could hear them still shouting, their cars starting. My main concern was the bleeding on the side of her head. She needed medical care. At one point I fought the nausea and weakness I always experienced at the sight of blood and took a closer look. I tore some of her blouse that was in shreds and used it to try to stop the bleeding. Then I realized that I had no idea how to get back to our home. So I told her she was safe there and to be patient. I was going to get some help. She shook her head violently NO, but I explained that she should not move because of the bleeding. "I have to go get some help. Have faith," I said. When she finally calmed down, I left and progressed a lot faster. I realized I was not too far from the shop. I had gone in a large circle. I went across the street and found my two uncles sick with worry. I briefly told them what had happened, where the girl was and how weak she seemed to be. They suggested I bring her as close as I could and we agreed on two signals; one to cross over and pick her up—the other in case of danger.

I went back to her, but she did not move. A dreadful feeling came over me: maybe she had bled to death. Her pulse was weak. She was either unconscious or asleep from exhaustion. So I ran back and weaved the signal meaning "Help." Carefully Pipo and Lino, one at a time, crossed the road and crawled toward me. I led them to where she lay and after a while they finally had her lying on a bed of wood shavings in the shop.

My mother and my aunt came into the shop with a flashlight and wet towels. They tried to clean her body with warm water. Our house was heated with a wood-buring stove and to avoid headaches we kept a pot filled with water. The girl could not be taken into the house because we did not want the children to see her. They might talk later when they were questioned. She was still in shock though warm blankets wrapped her body. My relatives did not think she was in danger; she could wait to see the doctor the next day. I was in charge of watching from the outside. Later I was told she had cigarette burns on her body. My mother had applied salve on the burns. One of us would stay with her in the shop and someone else would be outside on watch. She had come to, but was not talking. I had seen her around. She was my brother's age, no longer in school. Her family lived in town, but there was no way to let them know where she was. The curfew by now was on and we were forced to wait for the next day.

It was decided that I would deliver a bill to Roger the butcher and tell him to have someone take her to the doctor. We needed to alert her family but we did not know her name and she had not said a word. I did not go to school that day. I stayed home and slept. I had been up all night. Besides they were going to let her wear my coat with my pass and cover her head when she went to the doctor. I never found out how she ended up in that villa and the cause of that kind of trouble.

The FFI managed to get her taken care of and to warn her parents, who whisked her off to the country to some distant relative.

One thing very hard to believe was the fact that while some of our government leaders were a source of shame, most of the citizens were up in arms, extremely dedicated, determined to help people in any way they could. If it had not been for people like them, casualties would have been more dramatic. Would this support, this dedication of a human being for another be true today? I honestly don't know. All I know is that it was true then, no strings attached.

The Blue Ring

My Brother, Nini

After my departure from *Perpignan* my grandmother Teresa was placed into a retirement home since she needed constant care. Not too long there-after, my grandfather followed suit. My father, who was driving a truck for a delivery company continued his double schedule. He used the cover of his job to deliver food, medical supplies and even ammunition to the "Maquis". Nini, who was attending school, was left home alone more and more. Being very concerned, my mother asked my father again to let Nini come and live with us in *Marignane*. My father, however, was adamant and continued to refuse.

I knew Nini would not be satisfied until he succeeded to be part of the action. He was good at operating a radio, knew English and was extremely resourceful. On the other hand, the FFI organization was still in its early stages. There were lots of different groups not communicating between the units because of the lack of coordination and leadership.

The mail between Nini and I had been pretty steady at first, but I couldn't learn much. He was being very cautious because all correspondence was cen-sured. Then for a while the mail altogether stopped. My mother and I began to worry but we hoped it was just a delay with everything in such a turmoil. All we could do was pray and have faith all was well with Nini. Several

Above on the left one of the locations of the "Maquis" (always on the move).

months later, one letter arrived with no return address. The letter was from Nini and my father and informed us that they had moved from the *Pyrenées* (Perpignan area) and were now in a small town on the water, a little way from where we used to live. They were, however, soon on their way to the property up the mountain. The letter continued to say that things were pretty much the same. My father had the same type of job as before which was very involved and time consuming. Nini, now seventeen years old, had graduated and received his diploma (B.E.) and was now out of school. He was planning to go to work for the same company as his father. He had learned to drive and his two majors in school were paying off.

The translation of this was: they had moved back to the *Riviera*, near *Saint Raphael* and were on their way to the "Maquis" in the mountains. Nini's two majors that were now paying off were English, radio transmissions and cryptography. He also informed us that we did not need to write because he received information through his job and would keep in touch since he would be always on the go like father. From time-to-time we would be informed through the *Reséau,* the communication service for the underground *"tout va bien"* (all's well). We had no choice but to be happy with that.

The FFI were doing all they could to undermine the Germans. Bridges were blown up as well as railroads, trains loaded with military equipment, trucks transporting supplies to Germans, even our own refineries were destroyed. Everything was done to keep the Germans from getting the fuel they so desperately needed. The FFI wanted to save that fuel for the Americans but there seemed to be no way to do it. Reprisals were horrifying-fifty civilian lives for one German.

The FFI were also waiting for the Americans so they could join them. The French forces alone were not very strong to say the least. These forces were only strong on hope. They must have known or guessed something no one else did. A beach located between *St. Raphaël* and *St.Tropez* on the *French Riviera* was to become the landing site. The beach was situated in a remote area; it was not very large and its location was near the St. Raphael mountains chain, where the underground group had been in operation since day one.

Normandy had already taken place and the operation was known as 'Anvil'.

Through private sources we learned of Nini's promotions and were told that he had become a very valuable asset to the French underground, traveling extensively.

My uncles had a telephone in the shop before the occupation by the Germans. However it had been eliminated when they had been arrested earlier. Later on they managed to reconnect the line only, it was in a shack, on the back of the shop, where they kept limber, saw dust, wood shavings etc.. It was not used very often, only on emergencies. Once or twice my father, who didn't contact us very often, would call to see if anyone had been in touch with Nini. This indicated to us that father did not know where he was. We would then assume that Nini was off on a mission and naturally we would worry until someone would call and tell us *"tout va bien"* (all is well). I can recall how hard those days were on us. Among our other tribulations with the war, the fear of losing a loved one was always there. After a while, however, we had to learn to discipline ourselves not to think or we would actually go crazy.

Because of the secrecy of his missions, his letters became more and more scarce. We had no idea where he was and the closeness we enjoyed at one time, was replaced by worry and unrest. My father would never check to see how we were, nor would he report to us anything about Nini. All the messages we usually received, "Tout va bien", were always originating from Nini indirectly and if he were on a mission, we had no way of knowing what was going on. All we needed to know was that he was well.

Therefore, much of what did happen during these years since he had joined the underground was foreign to us, my mother and I.

Once Nini managed a brief visit to my mother and I.
This is the last picture I had taken with him.

Nini

Meanwhile Back In Italy

For years we lost touch entirely with Mémé Catérina. She had remained all alone in *Perinaldo* where all of the bridges accessing the village from *Ventimiglia* had been mined and declared off-limits. The only way that she could go to the city was by walking several miles up toward *Monte Bigone*, a very high mountain in the Alps. Before the climb would get steep, she would turn left into a little tourist village called *San Romolo* where she could board a "teleferique" (cable car) that would take her down to *San Remo* on the *Italian Riviera*. Then she would return the same way. The system worked the same as it does today. There were two cable cars, one going up and one coming down. When an air raid would occur, the electricity was immediately turned off and the two cable cars would stop and just hang until the air raid was over.

mémé Catin

Mémé Catérina had taken to knitting socks for the soldiers. At this time circular needles were nonexistent so she used three needles on the diameter of the sock and one to go around, being very sharp at each edge. When the cable car stopped in the middle of an air raid, everyone on board was very frightened. The planes would go around and around, missing the cable, so it seemed, by a miracle. Mémé Catin would knit faster and faster to calm her nerves. The other people finally would notice her speed and say, "Catin, slow down!" and they would all be distracted from their fears for that short moment. Then the air raid would end and Mémé Catin would put away her knitting, catch her breath and say, "Well, we made it another day!" This is something I inherited from her. Whenever I get upset, I knit incessantly to distract myself from my problems.

This is the teleferique mémé Catin would take from San Romolo to San Remo.

About the same time that Valerino was sent to Russia, Mémé Catérine had to deal with all kinds of unexpected events, trials and tribulations. One event that was most prevalent was when Mémé Catérina's home was requisitioned by the Germans. When these Germans came to set up station in this region of the Alps, they decided that Perinaldo would be the ideal location. Moreover, Mémé Catérina's home was the best choice since she had one of the nicest homes in Perinaldo. They were supposed to be Italy's allies, but they were there to make sure that the Italian Government and the citizens would follow orders. The officers took the third floor and part of the second floor and the soldiers occupied the ground floor, leaving a very small apartment for my grandmother on the second floor, which later became my inheritance. Mémé Catérina continued to go to the fields with Nina, her old donkey. Nina was very temperamental. No one could stand behind her except Mémé Catérina who would have to keep talking to her. Toward the end of the occupation things were getting pretty tough along with the lack of food and supplies. Somehow the Germans cut the fence and got hold of Nina. She went wild, kicking with all of her strength. She ended up seriously injuring two Germans. Mémé Catérina assumed that they probably killed her, since she was never seen again.

When the war with Italy became a faît accompli, Mussolini, knowing very well that the soldiers from Italy would refuse to fight their brothers on the other side of the French border, decided to send them instead to Russia to help the Germans. Valerino, like all of the Italian soldiers was far from being prepared to fight the hostilities, let alone the weather. He was fighting on the German side (in accordance with the agreement Mussolini had made to Hitler). The soldiers did not want to fight, they were Italians, this was not their war. Food was scarce, temperatures were extremely low, the uniforms they wore were very skimpy with only one small blanket in their backpack.

They were divided into two armies with different uniforms. The Fascists who were on Mussolini's side wore black shirts and were called the "Camicie Nere". These were the people that associated with Hitler. The other army, the Army of the King wore uniforms slightly different in shape, the color was between a shade of green and kaki and wore the emblem of a star. This army had been forced by the Fascists to follow the "Camicie Nere". The king did not want to fight, especially along with the Germans.

Without any hesitation, the Russians would shoot down all of the "Camicie Nere" in sight. Valerino was part of the King's Army and wore the star. This I'm sure contributed to the fact that he was spared in the battle of the "Don". Ricardo, his friend and next door neighbor, had been recruited at the same time in the same battalion. After a miserable lengthy walk, under the worse circumstances possible, they arrived on the opposite side of the river "Don" in Russia where they were met with a fierce attack by the Russians, whose main aim was the "Camicie Nere". Both armies were stopped because the river was frozen and they lacked proper equipment. Not only could they not cross but they could not see with the awful blizzard conditions, not to mention that the cold temperatures were paralyzing. The Russians nearly razed the "Camicie Nere"; the King's Army was spared and allowed to retreat in an outstanding confusion.

Valerino became lost; he walked endlessly in the blowing snow, became very ill due to frost bite and probably would have died if it wasn't for a Russian family who came to his rescue. They found him just in time, taking him to their home and nursing him back to health. For two to three months (he had lost track of time) they treated him like one of their own. Later he would thank his "lucky star", meaning the King's Army's uniform bearing the star. This family was aware of the difference between the two armies. Finally he was able to join back into some unit who shipped him home. For the rest of his life, he praised these people who had saved his life. He liked to say there were good people everywhere. One just had to look for them. Only he had not looked for this Russian family, they had found him, unconscious.

Meanwhile back in Perinaldo, Mémé Catérina and Pietro would visit each other encouraging, hoping, praying, and exchanging the latest news. Their children had to be alive! There was no doubt in their minds or so they would say. Once they were alone, however, in their respective homes, the doubt would creep in. When Valerino finally returned home, the entire family was relieved.

Since Valerino had returned both became more hopeful for Ricardo and shortly thereafter, he was found and returned home. Ricardo, however, had been seriously wounded, moving from one hospital to another for several months. No one can describe the happiness of the two older family members Pietro and Mémé Catérina. They wore constant smiles on their faces. After a period of time for the two to recuperate, Valerino and Ricardo had the time of their lives. Since they were both musicians, they played their music, drank wine and serenaded women all over the village. They were really the heroes: they had returned. When I later asked to know the details, they would suddenly become very serious and would just shake their heads. What they had seen, they wanted to forget. Their terrible experience in Russia marked them both for life. They were never the same.

For almost five years, we in France had no idea if both Mémé Catérina and Valerino were still alive. They in turn did not know if we were alive. Mémé Catérina had five children and several grandchildren in France. We were about three hours away on the other side of the border, but it seemed as if we were on another continent.

Valerino and Ricardo went back to work in the fields at their own pace, always with fear to be recalled. Italy was having all kinds of shortages just as we were in France. The shortage of salt, however, was something of a surprise to me and to my amazement, they had a lot of rice. To this day I never figured out why.

All her life, Mémé Catérina had made her living raising grapes and olives. They were then made into wine and olive oil and were sold along with her beautiful mimosa and flowers. During the years of the war, however, the fields had been neglected for lack of manpower. All she was able to raise were some vegetables to eat. Therefore her income had nearly vanished. Valerino and she had to start all over again.

Henri's Escape

Just before the war began, Tante Honorine had remarried and moved to Marseille, France with her two daughters Liliane and Emma. Her new husband, Antoine, was very short (about 5 feet tall), with bushy eyebrows and rough facial features. He appeared very mean and intimidating but was actually very kindhearted and easygoing. When I came to visit them in *Marseille* he loved to escort me and show me the sights. I always felt embarrassed because I was so tall and skinny and I seemed even more so when I stood next to him. Sometimes I would walk in the street while he walked on the sidewalk. He never seemed to notice. Antoine truly had a heart of gold and never was bothered by the small stuff. He was funny and I just adored him. To me he had all of the characteristics I always wanted my father to have, strict but caring. Antoine owned a couple of buildings in the old part of town and rented them out. Both he and my aunt ran the rental properties and made a good living. Their daughters, Liliane and Emma, had become beautiful girls. Liliane was an excellent seamstress and Emma was working in a department store. Emma was barely eighteen when she met Henri, fell in love and eventually married in the spring of 1941.

In June of 1941, Henri was picked up at work by the Germans and shipped to Germany. From the minute he boarded the train on that fateful day, Henri had no other thought than escape. He was first sent to the camp at *Strashof*, which was on the border of *Austria* and *Hungary*, where he was put to work in a farm that was an absolute nightmare. He knew he had to get out or he would die.

The most important thing, however, was to get transferred first. His father, Gabriel Luque, had worked for the S.N.C.F. (French Railroad) in *Marseille* for many years and had climbed to the envious position of superintendent of the Freight Marshaling Yard. With Henri's strength and determination, he somehow managed to convince the Germans that he knew all about railroads. (Having been a very good listener at the dinner table while growing up was now paying off. He had picked up many professional terms and various information when his father would relate some events which had happened to him while working at the railroad station). While in the *Strashof Farm* he tried to remember all that he had heard during his years at home. He would lay awake at night planning his strategy. He continued to show good will and the Germans finally decided that they needed someone like him. So they transferred him to *Amstetten* (*Austria's* Freight Marshaling Yard). He was put in charge of overlooking the shipping of freight. He was constantly under German surveillance and at night was taken to some other camp, just to return back to the job site the next day. Since he followed orders and minded his own business, the Germans began to be more at ease with him.

In the meantime, Emma relinquished her little apartment and had moved in with Henri's parents. She was too young to live alone while waiting for Henri to return and with the air raids becoming "around-the-clock events", it was nice to be near family. Besides, she felt like she could learn more news about Henri's fate living nearer to the people who worked at the railroad station. This railroad crowd, known as the "Cheminots", was very strong in the Resistance. It was separate from the underground, but just as knowledgeable and efficient. Everyday they managed to help some people escape. Their Reséau was endless. It not only covered France, but Italy and Spain as well.

As I mentioned before, I lived in Marignane, the airport for Marseille which was only 15 kilometers away from this city. Every three months or so I would go visit my Uncle Antoine and my Aunt Honorine. I had to apply for a pass at the German headquarters and this short trip took a very long time with all of the detours and stops at all of the checkpoints. Sometimes the bus would stop in the middle of nowhere just so the Germans could search the bus and ask for papers.

On one occasion, I recall arriving later in the evening. I got off at the Place d'Aix and walked the short distance to the old part of town where my aunt and uncle lived. In one of the buildings they owned, they rented the bottom floors and used the third and fourth floors for themselves. The only way to get in was to buzz and once someone saw you from the upper floors, they would release a button to let you in. This time I had planned to remain two days and I had all kinds of instructions from my uncles and my mother, all kind of news to report and collect.

That night when I arrived, we stayed up and talked until quite late. Their apartment was very small, so I slept on the divan in the living room. At about 5:00 a.m. the next morning, the doorbell rang. The Germans were known for arresting people during the middle of the night or at the crack of dawn for absolutely no reason. Many people that were arrested like this were never to be seen again. So when the doorbell rang, we all froze, jumped out of bed, got dressed, caught our breath and just looked at each other. One of us had to go down to the *rez-de-chaussée* (the ground floor) because it was still dark and we could not see who was ringing the doorbell. My Uncle Antoine went down the stairs with a big frown on his face. He looked ready for battle, while my aunt and I stood at the top of the winding stairs and tried to hear what was going on.

Finally, my Uncle Antoine came back up the stairs. The exchange at the door had taken less than five minutes. It turned out to be a young kid at the door, who looked very frightened and whispered something to my uncle and then disappeared in the dark. When Antoine finally caught his breath, he told us that the kid was a messenger from the Resistance "Cheminots" and that something important had happened. He was ordered to go to Henri's parents immediately. Henri's father Gabriel was still superintendent of the freight station in *Marseille* and had acquired more stripes to his rank. Right next to the Gare de *Marseille* (the railroad station) was an ugly building which had been taken over by the Germans. This run-down structure was now the German Headquarters, as well as a prison where thousands of people were interrogated, some tortured and then their fate was decided. From there they would ship the lucky ones to various German camps. This was where my two uncles, Pipo and Lino, had been taken earlier. It actually was everyone's nightmare. Many horror stories were floating around about the German Headquarters and no one wanted to think about it.

Antoine had to go and get in touch immediately with Gabriel, Henri's father. He was to give him a number and they had to contact someone at that number immediately. It seemed that Henri was in transit and in extreme danger.

The "Cheminots" had called and left instructions, but they were releasing these instructions to Gabriel only; he alone could get Henri out of the station using his position of superintendent.

That entire morning Aunt Honorina and I were waiting. Looking out of the window there was no way to know anything and nowhere to go to find out.

Later in the day Uncle Antoine came back, he looked relieved and exhausted, but he was full of news.

Apparently Henri had recruited several other prisoners, attending to the tiniest detail. He had done his homework. He learned that the watch dogs could not smell through paper, so he waited for a shipment of paper to test this theory out. He knew he had only one chance. Some of the other prisoners got scared and bailed out of this chance to freedom. This left only Henri and two others. They entered the rail cars filled with bags of paper. Then they heard the doors being locked and the Germans used the lead to seal the cars. They knew that this was it, their only chance. For five days they laid on the bottom of the rail cars without a single morsel of food or drop of water. All they had was some sugar that they had somehow managed to acquire and from time-to-time they would take a little nibble to keep their strength. They finally arrived in *Paris*.

The *Cheminot* Resistance were there to save people once they got in contact through a window covered with wires on the side of the freight railroad car. They managed to move the trains doing all kinds of maneuvering. They also cut the wires around the windows, passing bread and water through it and telling the passengers to jump when a certain signal was displayed. At the intended signal, Henri jumped on the railroad track next to the train. Being weak he fell on his knees. Right where he jumped, a German guard was there with a firearm aimed at him. Both Henri and the German guard made eye contact with each other. Henri made a sign throwing his arms in the air as if to indicate that he had tried to escape but was now surrendering. Suddenly, the German guard lowered his gun and turned around. Then Henri began to run followed by the two others who disappeared in another direction. Henri never heard of or saw the other two again.

It is more than likely that some other "Cheminots" took care of them. They had to go separate ways and be divided to avoid attracting attention. From Paris Henri was sent to a little freight marshaling yard in a small town called *Vierzon Couré*. Here the Resistance prepared a banquet for him and he ate so much at this event he became very ill.

From there he was transferred by train towards *Marseille*. The *"Cheminots"* managed to send word to Henri's father. The train was to arrive between the Hotel Terminus on the right and the German Headquarters on the left in *Marseille*. My Uncle Antoine was on his way to make sure that Gabriel, Henri's father, knew that his son had arrived. Somehow the "Cheminots" had kept in touch with Gabriel while the train was in route, but when the delays occurred, no one knew where they were. At the same time that the train Henri was on board arrived, another train was getting ready to leave for the camps. This one was completely full of prisoners, locked into freight cars, just like animals. It also carried food, ammunition and valuables that they were taking from the museums as well as peoples' homes, which they had confiscated, back to their "Beloved Germany".

With both trains in front of the headquarters this became an extremely risky situation. To have gone through all that Henri had endured through this trip and to be caught now was unthinkable. This was where Gabriel came into the picture. Being in charge of the Freight Marshaling Yard he ordered several "maneuvres" on various trains, while Henri remained in the train until the FFI came through the Hotel Terminus. Casually they directed him into a secluded area, handed him some clothes and whispered instructions. Quickly he put them on and very unassumingly walked out of the hotel with no one noticing. He walked along the street as if he had not a worry in the world, made several detours and reached a special area where he was to be picked up.

Antoine had followed him from a distance and saw that he was picked up. Someone would contact us later.

This was definitely a rejoicing time.

....

Now all we had to do was to be extremely careful and continue to act as before Henri's rescue.

Therefore Emma continued to live with Henri's parents while Henri was placed in hiding. The Resistance was sensational! How they could whisk Henri from the station out to the country directly under the Germans' noses was beyond me. Having plenty to tell them, Henri was debriefed by the Resistance for days and the most meaningless detail was analyzed.

The FFI were also watching Henri's parents as well as Emma and her family. They were afraid of reprisals from the Germans. We thought of cutting my trip short but decided it would attract attention. Once all seemed to be safe and clear, my Aunt Honorine sent me back home to tell everyone what had happened. This was a trip I was anxious to take as I was the bearer of good news for a change.

Henri remained in hiding for a very long time, only interrupted by frequent, quick changes of location in the middle of the night, always disguised. Henri's brother-in-law was a "Sapeur Pompier of *Marseille*" (a fireman of Marseille). The Germans respected the firemen because they did a tremendous job during the air raids, saving so many people's lives including the Germans'. Because of this the Germans never bothered the firemen with papers so Henri was given a "Sapeur Pompier" uniform. Many times he used to go to various locations where he was needed disguised in this uniform. Once during an alarming event, the Resistance decided to dress him up as a woman. This state of affairs was extremely hard on everyone's nerves. Everybody became very short tempered, jumpy and if the truth was known, extremely afraid.

More than ever we were praying for the Americans to land.

Marseille

Closing In

Closing In

The tension around us, all over the country and especially in Marignane was increasing. The war was escalating at an incredible speed. The BBC was full of hope and encouragement. "Be patient. Soon it will be over," they would say. Meanwhile the Germans on the French controlled radio stations were announcing success on the battle fronts.

Everyone was whispering about the Allied landing. They were trying to guess where and when this was going to happen. One thing we knew for sure was that the Germans were running out of gasoline.

Beyond the airport was the town of *Berre*. Since the refinery had been demolished, and some of the railroad had been destroyed, the Germans had turned to another refinery in the area called *"La Mede"* located across the water on the opposite side of *Berre*. This refinery did not produce a lot of gasoline but the Germans were desperate for it, no matter how little the quantity. They feared that the Allies would bomb *"La Mede"* so they tried to fill as many tankers as were available. Tankers, however, were pretty hard to hide while waiting to be moved toward the battlefront where tanks were abandoned because of the lack of petrol.

Then the Germans decided to try and salvage some the *Berre's* railroad and move the gasoline to a storage in this area where they thought the Allies would not return. Immediately they began working day and night on a track that would connect *"La Mede"* into a small storage area near *Berre*, which had survived the air raids. They used prisoners, soldiers and just about anyone they could get their hands on. Meanwhile, the FFI was very aware of what was going on and kept extremely busy. From our shop we kept a close watch and with the few contacts we had delivering our hardware, we made lots of connections and the trips to Roger's store increased. Roger had decided to do some more remodeling which helped us all keep our cover. For a while my trips had been directed to the bakery a few doors down and a Mercerie, (where they sold sewing supplies, etc.). The owner of the Mercerie also had decided she needed more shelving space and consulted my uncles on how to do this job.

The Mercerie was very old fashioned. I actually never noticed the shop before I started to deliver the hardware for the shelving. It was in the same area as Roger's store but on a different street. The owner was a middle-aged widow who was very nondescriptive, stern and distant. She was not one to take up a conversation, so our meetings were extremely short. At one point I remember asking for thread to match some piece of material since my mother was a seamstress. I could return the thread and get another one without a problem. This incident happened constantly and I'm sure there was some underlying meaning to this - perhaps a code to the Resistance. This was

March of 1944. At that point a middle age man came to stay at the Mercerie to help the owner. He was a distant cousin to Louise (this was the only name I knew). He could not find work where he lived in the Alps so the story was that he did the remodeling for room and board. In actuality, he was a member of the Underground planted there getting ready for something to happen.

Finally the railroad connection was all finished and one night my two uncles and I spent hours watching the tankers being transferred to the previously defunct storage station. When I went to school the next morning, I was told to deliver a bill to all three shops. This was billing time. We also wanted to make sure there was no mix up. School started at 8:00 a.m. so I had to be by the shops a little before this in order not to be late for my classes. Unfortunately, two of the shops were still closed. I hand delivered the first bill, announcing this was billing time. Then I knocked on the doors of the other two shops but there was no answer. I ended up walking to the entrance of the apartment where they lived and slid the bill under the door.

That night I had to take my accounting class at the Terra's mansion. On my arrival, I noticed that the Germans on the ground floor were extremely busy and seemed very nervous. Some were shouting on the telephone, furiously screaming in the receiver on one side trying to get the attention from the switchboard on the other. For the first time no one asked to see my pass. So I went upstairs to class. There I found the three sisters who were so exhausted they looked as if they were at the point of collapse. However no words were exchanged. As the noise downstairs continued and at one point began to increase, we could not concentrate in our class. For the hundredth time I regretted not having taken German in school. I wanted so desperately to understand what they were saying and know what was going on. We were afraid to leave early and attract attention. However it finally got so out of hand that we were asked to leave by our instructors. This was about 8:30 p.m. and it was pitch-dark outside. I gladly left this madhouse. Every time I came to the Terras' for class I constantly feared that the Allies would bomb the house since it was actually the German Headquarters.

On my walk home, I barely turned onto the Boulevard du Nord when the siren started to howl. That sound always had a terrible effect on me. When this particular siren went off, I had not yet crossed the line at the checkpoint and I had no idea where to go. Once the siren would go on, no one was allowed to go beyond the line and I really did not have much desire to be the first to do it, since I was going toward the area being bombed. Right before the end of the boulevard where the roads separated there was an incredible amount of trucks and vans of all kinds guarded by Germans.

Midway on the boulevard there was a little side street which ran into a dirt road that in turn led to the backside of our property. My only chance would be if I got lucky and could go around, avoiding the Germans. Fortunately the traffic was very heavy on the paved streets. Still I was terrified that the Germans would see me. They were known to shoot first and ask questions later. I had to reach deep inside of myself and find all the courage I could to cross these fields and get home safely.

I decided to go into the street, crawling against the walls, stopping to listen, and then starting again. I was lucky that I was wearing my ugly yellow-green coat made from an army blanket; it served as a camouflage. The street was not very long and eventually it ended, as did the dirt. Now all I had to do was cross it and go to the fields with no protection on either side. I debated if I should lay in the ditch and wait out the air raid. That, however, did not appeal to me. I knew my family was worried about me so I decided to proceed.

In the air I could see the search lights looking for planes. Shooting was going on in every direction. The sky was crisscrossed with deadly fire from all of the ground artillery firing. Intermittently there were explosions randomly occurring. Just before I had a chance to cross the fields, one terrible explosion ripped the countryside. Somehow I found myself lying in a ditch. I decided to stay there. (Actually I was so shaken that I could not have moved even if I had wanted to.)

More explosions followed in the same direction. They, however, were not as loud or as big as the initial one or so I thought. By now I was getting immune to these explosions. They were beginning to be more and more a part of my everyday life. Soon, in the foreground, I could see smoke going up from the gigantic flames that the explosions had made. It seemed so close but actually these fires were toward the town of *Berre*. With all of the uproar, one didn't know which direction was the safest. Some ground fire was coming from the vicinity near our home. I laid there in the unkept field, all scratched up with debris clinging to every part of my coat, trying to decide what to do next. This was difficult since I was now dizzy from repeatedly throwing myself on the ground through all of the explosions. After I recovered a little, I decided to proceed and started creeping through the fields. Luckily the Germans were all preoccupied and concentrating on the explosions, so they didn't notice me or else didn't care.

I cannot even begin to describe that "field walk" home. I would keep saying to myself, "Wake up!! You are just dreaming!" This, however, was no dream. It was a living nightmare! For the longest time I continued the crossing, crawling through bushes, dead grass and at one point, I even landed in a puddle of water. As if this was not enough, I continued to brush aside the thought that this field might be mined. I finally reached the small, neglected field that crossed to our shelter. I found, however, that it was impossible to cross from that direction. My uncles had seen to it that we would be protected from surprises that could occur from this side of the field. So I laid still until the siren rang the "all clear warning" and still waited until the traffic on the main road slowed down. Everything on wheels was headed for the fire. This was no time to be caught, not that a certain time was better than another. I finally found a break in the traffic, came up the dirt road to the shelter just as everyone was coming out. Needless to say I received a tremendous welcome from my family.

The night of my lucky, heroic return home, I remember it was 2:00 a.m.

when I finally looked at a clock. All of a sudden I realized how starved I was. As usual we were short of food. I would have loved some milk and bread, but that was for the three little kids. Milk was a luxury and our bread ration had been eaten for dinner. We were allowed a slice a day and if you know the French, they could very well eat a loaf a day. Being starved was a normal, everyday event in our life. One ate whatever was available at any time, because later you may not eat for a long period of time. In short, you ate when you had it since you never knew when your next meal would be. That night, I ended up eating a piece of raw fruit or vegetable. To top matters, my coat was muddy and I had been scratched from falling and throwing myself onto the ground. I had stickers all over me and I was cold, tired, and hungry. I was safe, however, and that was all that really mattered.

All throughout the night there was commotion on both roads. Sounds from continual explosions, shouting on the roads and massive fires on the ground accompanied by smoke filled the skies. We had a good idea what was going on since we had caused this situation in a very small way.

The next morning our guesses were confirmed. The Allies had bombed all of the tankers that the Germans had filled with gasoline. The storage station that the Germans had so recently built was totally destroyed. Fires were all over the hills and it took a lot of manpower to put them out. The Germans were feverishly trying to protect their own supplies (which were really our supplies that they had confiscated) and the few civilians who were left were trying to keep the fire away from their dwellings.

This became the turning point in our lives. By then it was not uncommon to experience three to five air raids during one day. As this continued and eventually escalated, these continual interruptions were taking most of the time away from the actual studies of the students. Therefore, schooling was then held underground in the shelters. This may have been safer without the Germans interrupting the classes, but it did not feel any less frightening. The

lighting was terrible with only little light bulbs hanging here and there. Moreover, the ventilation was extremely poor and the atmosphere was eerie. No one could concentrate and many of the students became ill. I am surprised that anyone could learn anything while underground or for that matter, above the ground.

Marignane

106

The Liberation

Finally, many days after it happened we learned of the Normandy landing. We were delighted and yet extremely worried to hear it was a very bloody battle and we hoped for the best. Everyone was praying for the success of the landing. This was in June. We expected changes but they did not happen. The battle was raging in *Normandy* and *Brittany* and it seemed it was headed for Germany instead of toward us in the south. It was understandable that they were trying to push the Germans back to where they came from.

In the south, the Underground was extremely busy. We did not hear anything at all from Nini and were wondering where he may be. The days seemed to drag on more than usual. The waiting was far more unnerving. Air raids continued, but it was different. There seemed to be less Germans, perhaps they had been sent where they were sorely needed like *Normandy*. Casualties were heavy on both sides. We really did not know much about the battles. We had no way to know. The enemy had their own propaganda on the French radio and no one turned it on. From the BBC we would get brief news and encouragement, however to listen to them was an ordeal, someone had to be on watch.

American Cemetery at Normandy.

Then things began to change. The landing had been successful but the battles in the north were fiercer than ever. This was August. For some odd reason the French people began to feel hope, the Allies were on French soil. Their dream had come true! *Normandy*, however, was a long way from *Marseille*. Even so, the fact that they were near helped enormously. We had to keep our

Following the Normandy landing here is the Liberatoin of Paris above and right.

emotions in check because the Germans became very touchy and suspicious.

At that point the town officials announced that the alarms were not going to be sounded anymore since they felt that the people were in constant danger. They suggested that everyone stay in the shelters as much as possible until further notice. Most of the shops closed, the schools closed and everything came to a standstill. For a couple of weeks it became very quiet, just like before a storm. At the time we believed that all of the German forces were up north trying to fend off the Allies and we began to take less precautions. Then, however, there was a terrible bombing. This time the target was on the hills above the town where the Germans had built a fortress. We were told to stay away from the town if at all possible. There was no telling what the Germans

would do. If they had to withdraw, there was no defense, civilian or otherwise. Moreover, there were no police or young men around since most of them were working for the Underground. All that was left were women, children and the elderly.

One tragic event took place in a small town only thirty kilometers from us. In a rage, the Germans arrested all of the children, women and elderly people

Paris clockwise from top left: Eiffel Tower, Sacré Coeur, fountain, and arc de Triomphe.

and locked them up in a church. There, they set fire to them all. One woman had thrown her four year old son out of the window and he was the only survivor out of 139 people. The horror of this massacre made everyone furious, yet more cautious. So everyone remained close to the shelters. I was home with the rest of the family. The shop was closed and we were all idle, just waiting.

After several days of isolation and ignorance we just had to know what was taking place and the only way was for me to go to town. I tried to tell my family that there was nothing to fear; all was quiet, I could easily go and find out. They objected since we were told to stay in and that was final.

The next morning I once more tried to change their minds, I told them this was ridiculous. Nothing was going on and I was the only one who could go, having all kinds of passes. I finally succeeded in convincing them. I was given all kinds of instructions; if I was stopped, I could come up with some logical excuse. So around 9:30 that morning, I started toward town.

When I arrived at the checkpoint on Boulevard du Nord, it was deserted. I could see that all of the doors were closed and all the shutters sealed on every home and business in town. No one was in the streets and I almost turned to head back home in a moment of panic, but my curiosity got the best of me. So I proceeded farther down toward the center of town. When I came to the little side street giving access to the fields, I kept constantly on guard and looked in every direction to watch for Germans.

What I saw, however, was very unexpected. When I traveled this road in the past it had always been open and I could see to the end of the paved street and the beginning of the dirt road. Now it was blocked with trees which covered the entire road. After looking again at these unfamiliar trees, I noticed that they were moving. Not knowing what to do, I looked across the street and I saw Roger, the one in charge of the Underground walking in the opposite direction. He was not there a minute ago (where did he come from!). Without looking at me and gritting through his teeth, I vaguely heard him tell me, "Get out of the streets, now!" I really thought he was crazy since we were the only two in the streets. Nonchalantly, I told him, "Look at all of those trees!" Again he said, "Will you get out!" His very nasty tone really scared me so I immediately started to hastily walk away, doing my best not to run.

I tried to get into several stores along the way but they were all locked up. After trying three or four more shops I came to the doorway of a "Bar Tabacs" and I found myself being grabbed by several arms and pulled inside. The trees that I had seen in the road were actually masses of branches that were covering tanks and soldiers entirely for camouflage. They had branches covering them all the way from their helmets down to their army boots. Most important, however, was the fact that they were very quiet, progressing like ghosts. Thus began the Liberation of our town.

After *Normandy* we did not know how the Allied Forces would come to the south. *Normandy* was a wide-spread beach which was perfect for landing. In the south, however, the only beaches were on the *Riviera* and most of them were resorts. And these, of course, were occupied by the Germans. So it came as a complete surprise when they landed in a secluded beach near the St. Raphael Mountains.

Landing Beach August 15, 1944.

This plan was very successful since it was so unexpected with all of the enemy forces still concentrating on the north. Then we learned that this operation, which was called "Anvil" had been on and off during the spring of 1944. To confuse the German Intelligence in the final weeks before the landing, the operation name was changed from "Anvil" to "Dragoon" and General Dwight Eisenhower had been appointed Commander in Chief for the second front. From there he agreed with General Omar Bradley that it was vital to take Marseille as rapidly as possible. Marignane was the airport for Marseille and I could understand the haste to clear this area quickly, not only because Marseille had a large harbor, but it also had a very important railway system leading along the Rhone Valley toward Paris and the Alsace Lorraine area bordering Germany. My uncles had discussed that point many times but no one knew for sure.

The Canadian tanks were first to arrive, followed by the Algerian troops. Then later the Americans and finally the British arrived. When these tanks came into the main street of the town just like a miracle, some of the underground FFI showed up. People I hadn't seen for ages were in the streets. Every door was flung open and the French people were lavishly pouring champagne. Where all of this came from I never knew!

Square General Dwight D. Eisenhower

It was truly insane. Children, both boys and girls, were climbing on top of the tanks hugging the soldiers. Everyone was singing the national anthem and waving flags. I had seen this happening in the movies but this was our town. I really thought I was dreaming. The FFI, however, cut this euphoria short by ordering us all back home and told us to remain in hiding. This was because the Germans had not left, as far as they knew and they could have been anywhere. Why take any chances now when we had waited this long for freedom;

This is the Beech where it took place "Le Drammond".

what was a little more waiting going to do?

The FFI also informed us that all around the town and high in the hills the Germans had constructed a fort-like structure which contained large amounts of firearms, including long range ones to hit ships that were coming on the side of the water. These "canons" were the kind that rotate and could hit and destroy not only the strategic areas but could also destroy the town, killing many people. Revenge was the big threat to all of us and no one would be spared even if they tried to escape. The Allied Forces proceeded to head for the hills and make a thorough search in this area. Again they repeated to keep a low profile until the entire area had been searched and declared safe. No one seemed to listen and people continued to stay out in the open, celebrating until some shots were fired. Only then did the people comply. I went home as quickly as I could to let my family know what was happening. I passed the empty checkpoint for the second time that day. Looking sideways as I passed, not yet believing that the Germans had actually left. This was definitely a rejoicing occasion.

I remained home and everyone was talking about what was happening. I was getting restless, however, to see what else was going on in town. But my family insisted that I stay close to home. Later in the afternoon I couldn't stand it anymore and I convinced my mother and my uncles to let me go into town. I had to see if the place had been found secure by the Allies.

I crossed the town and went to the little square where Pilia's Grocery was located. When I got there, I learned that several soldiers had been wounded near the river a few yards away. The

MONUMENT INSCRIPTION
OVER THIS DEFENDED BEACH THE MEN OF THE 35TH U.S. INFANTRY DIVISION STORMED ASHORE 15 AUGUST 1944 TOGETHER WITH THEIR FRENCH ALLIES. THEY BEGAN HERE THE DRIVE THAT TOOK THEM ACROSS FRANCE THROUGH GERMANY AND INTO AUSTRIA TO THE FINAL DESTRUCTION OF THE GERMAN ARMIES AND THE NAZI REGIME.

The Blue Ring

CE MEMORIAL	This Memorial
CELEBRANT LE CENTENAIRE	Celebrating the Centenial
DE LA NAISSANCE DU	of the birth of
GENERAL CHARLES DE GAULLE	General Charles De Gaulle
A ETE REDIGE SUR LES LIEUX	has been created on the
MEMES DU DEBARQUEMENT	exact area of the landing
DES FORCES FRANCAISES LIBRES	of the French Free Forces
LE 15 AOUT 1944	August 15, 1944
ET INAUGURE LE 2 JANVIER 1991	and inaugurated on the Jan. 2, 1991
PAR MONSIEUR LE SENATEUR	by The Senator
CHARLES PAQUA	Charles Pasqua
MAITRE ANDRE CHARLES BLANC	and Master Andre Charles Blanc
CONSEILLER GENERAL	General Councellor
ETANT MAIRE	Being Mayor.

news was unchanged, we had to remain undercover. Some of the people volunteered to help with the wounded so an arm band was provided for them with a Red Cross. Everyone was acting patriotic. There was also an air of elation even with the sense of danger still existing about the whereabouts of the Germans. I knew better than to help with the Red Cross since I was not very strong when it came to the sight of blood. I would end up having someone help me since I would no doubt get sick after seeing it. Instead I was the only one who spoke English and an interpreter was needed. So I qualified for this position and was given an arm band with "Interpreter" written across it. At that time, however, I wasn't needed because the Liberating Forces were Canadians, Algerians and Morrocans who all spoke French.

Eventually I returned home wearing my arm band and related the latest instructions that I had received by the Allies and the FFI to my family. We were to remain in our shelters or very near them for several days. I also told my family about there being some wounded soldiers and one casualty.

After a couple of days during which Canadian tanks followed the Algerians and Morrocans, who were on foot, crawling along the hills with knives in their teeth, the area was pronounced safe. Nobody could imagine what relief we felt. This was a state of mind we had all forgotten for almost five long years. We had been living in fear. This feeling is too hard to describe in words, one had to have been there and lived those five years, day to day to understand. We became cautious, not believing anything we heard or trusting anyone.

I found myself on guard for years after our trauma and I am sure everyone who was involved also felt the same way. Living in constant fear had been a part of our lives and it would be a very hard habit to break.

Free At Last

After the Allied Forces had announced that the area was safe, they proceeded to continue their search and went north. This must have been the 28th or 29th of August. The city was without any kind of defense. Total euphoria was in the air and we were thrilled. There was something however that kept us a little uneasy and held us back. We were so used to having catastrophes occur that we expected one at any minute. We could not sleep even though there were no longer any air raids, there were no vehicles in the streets and everything was quiet. It was a very strange feeling. Moreover, no one was really working, the schools were closed and everything was in limbo.

In the afternoon of September 3rd, I was delivered a summons from the Mayor of *Marignane*. I had worked with him as a courier for the FFI so I was rather surprised to be officially summoned.

It read: *"Nous vous prions de bien vouloir, vous presenter au bureau de M. le Maire, le 4 Septembre à 10:00 heures, pour recevoir les 'Forces Alliees'."* This translated was as follows: "You are invited to be at the Mayor's office, September 4th at 10:00 a.m. to welcome the 'Allied Forces'."

I had to read the summons several times before I finally realized its meaning. My dream was coming true; I was finally going to work for the Americans! I started to dance around the house, waving my letter in the air and shouting, "I made it!" as the smiling faces of my entire family were there as my audience. No one could ever imagine the flurries of activities that took place following this news! I had to get myself together. The first order of business was my hair which was straight and long. Everyone agreed that I had to do something about my hair. After a shampoo, I proceeded to put on "bigoudis"; these were pieces of rags that you rolled your hair with, making a knot and then letting them set. Sometimes one left them in all night. After it dried completely the "bigoudis" would come off and there would definitely be curls.

Then my clothes had to be tried on several times. Unfortunately, all of the dresses that I had did not fit now. My mother had made me several dresses when I first arrived from the Pyrenées. I was very tall, thin and slight. After the Germans' invasion she had forbidden me to wear them. So she started to pull the sewing machine out and quickly whipped me up something. I even went to the extent to put light polish on my nails (first time ever). The entire household was full of activity, no one slept much and everyone wanted to be a part of it.

When I walked into the Mayor's office the next day, his sincere surprise and admiration lifted my heart. I was a nervous wreck and he restored my confidence when he said, "I would never have recognized you, what happened?" I smiled and said, "Just a miracle and I hope this is only the beginning."

Bridge in the vicinity of Marignane.

At that time a commotion was heard in the halls and we all came to attention. In came the American delegation along with some French officials. I was so overwhelmed that I hardly remember what was said. I was introduced around and questioned in English. I answered as well as I could. Fortunately I understood every word; however, I was aware that my pronunciation was terrible. One of the majors broke away from the group and led me toward a typewriter. He introduced himself as Major Shinn. He was going to be in charge of the new depot "Engineer Depot E-521". They were going to take over an old unused factory on the outskirts of town where there was a lot of land surrounding it. He asked several questions and told me to write everything down - both questions and answers. He also wanted to know how and why I had learned English. He had already been informed of my activities with the FFI. He smiled and said "When can you start?" I immediately replied, "Right now."

With a big grin he said,

"Your knowledge of the English language, especially your writing is excellent. Your pronunciation, however, will need to be improved." (This was a nice way of putting it) and he added,

"Consider yourself hired as of now. You are to report starting tomorrow at 8:00 a.m. A vehicle will be here in front of the City Hall to take you to the location. You will be in charge of recruiting French personnel. Everyday during your lunch hour you will report to the infirmary, where Captain Devereau, an American doctor of French/Canadian origin, will teach you the correct American pronunciation." Then he warmly smiled at me and held his hand out to shake mine and continued to say,

"Welcome! See you tomorrow." Tears sprang to my eyes, I was over-whelmed, unable to say anything I just nodded with a very shy smile.

After the meeting, I flew home. I had so many things to do to prepare for my new job. I had to get some more clothes planned, made, or altered. The afternoon frantically came and went. Later I realized that no one had men-tioned a "salary" to me. Even my own family hadn't questioned me about this, as if it was a small detail. At this time all that was really important to me was that my dream was finally coming true!

The next morning we were all up at 5:00 a.m. Everyone wanted to make sure that I was on time. I hadn't slept a wink. The excitement was too much. I was also worried that they would find me too young and I could see myself dismissed for lack of experience.

When I arrived at the City Hall, I boarded the vehicle with a large group of janitors that were instructed to clean our new offices. The location of this new depot was only about fifteen kilometers away. When we arrived, the first space cleaned was mine. It was really nothing to talk about. It had one desk with a broken chair. There were several pads of paper and pencils on the desk. This is how I started out.

The word had been passed around that this new American headquarters was looking to hire. Soon, there was a line of prospective workers outside of the building waiting to be interviewed. I proceeded to hire them as quickly as I could. Then I would assign them to an American sergeant standing by me, who in turn would direct them where they were needed. During this proce-dure I kept translating back and forth and I began to realize that I could not do all of the hiring and translating fast enough. Therefore, I first hired office personnel that I could put to work immediately. I had them making lists of the people who were waiting to be interviewed for work, their addresses, their profession and background and all of the other information required for hir-ing. This would save a lot of time; then the people who had completed these preliminary stages would wait to be interviewed by me. I would review their sheets of information that were presented to me, make the necessary transla-tions, ask additional questions if necessary, then I would turn them over to the sergeant who made the final decision and dispatched them accordingly.

In a matter of two weeks we had an office staff of forty-five. Most of these employees were women. In addition, we had close to one hundred employees in the labor section covering all types of special skills including electricians, plumbers, carpenters, etc. Since *Marignane* was small and had been almost deserted, the employees were brought in from *Marseille* by trucks. The offices were now completely furnished with the telephones operating in all areas. The mess hall was in full operation with meal schedules efficiently posted for soldiers, officers, etc. and another schedule for civilian employees.

The barracks were all set up to lodge the American troops in one part of the depot while in another area dwellings were also erected to take care of both German and Italian prisoners. The officers had other living facilities in town offered by the French people. This was to be a depot of surplus with every machinery imaginable available for the reconstruction of the damaged countries.

Much to my delight, my two uncles were hired to help organize the cabinet-making department. I had earlier mentioned my uncles to my supervisor about this position. I felt, however, it may have been against regulations to employ one's own relatives so I had turned this over to him. He gladly enrolled them to help with the organization of the cabinet making/carpentry department. I worked very hard and loved every minute of it. My supervisors were very happy with me and I, in turn was happy with them. When I think back, this must have been one of the happiest times of my life. The war was still going on up in the north of France, but we were free. There still lingered one dark cloud in our life at the present: we had no idea where Nini was.

Next to my office was the office of Lieutenant Dyke and two nice young men who were his aides. They were very friendly and they loved to play practical jokes and tricks on me. During the war leather was scarce so I had made a purse out of cardboard covered with a fabric. I thought I had done a very nice job. One day the three "Mousquetaires", (Muskateers - as I called them) decided to pull one of their tricks. I had been absent from my desk for just a few minutes but when I returned, I came back to find that my purse had been stapled together. I was not at all pleased but I tried to make "light of it" since I didn't want them to know how I really felt.

Several days later during lunch I was given a very large slice of bread. I decided to wrap it in paper, put it in my purse and take it home. The food situation had slightly improved, however, the Americans had no idea of the extreme shortage we were still experiencing. (Near the Motor Pool, in a rather deserted area, after the G.I.'s had finished with their meals they would find children waiting by the trash asking for their leftovers).

Nolan, one of the guys in the office next to mine, decided to grab my purse and run. When he got to his office he opened it, finding the bread and turned red right to his scalp. I too was extremely embarrassed since I had never mentioned to anyone the kind of problems we still had. After that, my purse was never touched and oddly enough, the mess hall began complaining about having too much food. Ironically they put me in charge of distributing it. From then on my family's life improved. The PX also would give us food rations with the excuse that they didn't want to keep it on the shelves for too long. Today, when I think of those events, tears still come to my eyes.

Working for the Americans I made more money than I ever dreamed. We were paid in dollars and with the exchange it was just wonderful. With my first pay check I purchased an almost new blue and white bicycle. I thought I was the richest girl in the world!

We were free to listen to the radio now but the broadcasts were still aired from occupied territories and it was simply propaganda. The BBC, however, kept up their good work, thank heaven.

Then in December we knew of the Battle of the Bulge. Just two weeks prior to this we had received a letter from Nini, who wrote how proud he was of my accomplishments, congratulating me on my new job with the Americans. He had joined the American forces where he was doing better and bigger things. He also mentioned that he was traveling a lot and was extremely happy.

My father made one of his rare phone calls and confirmed that Nini was now under American uniform and had been promoted. He could not really talk about it but he knew he was headed for a capital which we assumed was Paris. My mother asked him if it was dangerous and my father replied, "It is always dangerous, but I feel good about it."

In the meantime, I started to have a few problems with the office personnel. It seemed that I had hired some ladies whose secretarial skills were only a cover. There was also a lot of resentment between myself and some of the staff because they had to take the orders from me. I was the youngest, hence they were giving me a lot of trouble. During this time a man who spoke English was hired for the fields. He had to report to us in the main office everyday. After he had worked for us a short while he became cocky. One day he started to make blunt advances toward me and talking as if I were one of his so-called "proteges" insinuating that I was not so hard too comply with the night before. When I asked him to apologize, he grabbed my arm with his evil eyes leered at me. I insisted that he let go of my arms and he kept on trying to humiliate me; twisting my arm painfully. Various people in the office found this quite amusing. Showing off he had backed me against a desk. In a state of rage I reached out behind and grabbing an enormous stapler I hit him hard on his bald head. He had to be taken to the infirmary. Major Shinn, when informed of the incident, had sent one of his aides to talk to the man very sternly. The next day the ladies who had given me so much trouble were gone as well as the man. Later I discovered that this man was a pimp and the ladies worked for him as prostitutes.

One of the girls I hired to replace the quickly withdrawing ladies of the night was Raymonde. She had applied for a job with me and we became very good friends. She was lonely since she had just moved into the area and didn't know anyone. I mentioned her to my mother, who immediately invited her to come to visit us. Raymonde was very withdrawn and it took her a while before she accepted. Once my family met her they got along immediately and before we knew it, Raymonde became a regular to our house. By now we had resumed our normal life and Tante Yvonne decided we should remain at the villa, while she would find a place in downtown *Marignane* for her family. She was determined to move to town.

So it happened that Raymonde came to visit us every Sunday. She was very quiet and it took a long time to get her to talk about herself. She would always come with a pastry called St. Honore, which was my favorite; it was a small cake covered with a special cream, with little cream puffs nicely placed all around on top.

Raymonde had recently gone through a traumatic experience. She was living in a little village in the north of France with her mother who had been quite ill. After a particular bad spell, it looked like her mother was in need of a doctor immediately. She was so upset, however, that she forgot to take her pass with her. Her fiancé, with whom she was very much in love, offered to go with her. They both took their bikes and about half way to their destination she realized she was not wearing her pass, however he had his. The town was at some distance and to return home to get her pass they would have had to go another direction toward the German Headquarters. For some reason they decided his pass would be sufficient. As they arrived at a railroad crossing, there were Germans all over the place. Just prior to the couple's arrival, two guards had been blown up. The Germans were furious. Needless to say, this was a very bad place to be. Retaliation was always a scare. They lined up Raymonde's fiancé and fourteen others that were coming down the street and shot them down like mad dogs before her very eyes. Raymonde was taken to headquarters to explain the situation. She was finally released, her mother ended up dying and Raymonde remained alone for a very long time afterward. At one point she even had attempted suicide. She was hospitalized and after being released was offered shelter by the Red Cross. Instead she had come down through the occupied territory, walking, with just the clothes on her back, not caring whether she lived or died.

It would not be hard to guess the unbelievable amount of hatred the Germans had managed to earn. These kinds of reprisals happened quite often. It made the French people become bold, fearless, and emotionally numb. It took a long time for us to show Raymonde that there were good people in the world. I want to hope that we made a difference. For years she was treated as if she were a second daughter to my mother.

The Depot E-521 had become my life. However I must say that a lot was happening in the town of Marignane. After the disappearance of the Germans, a wind of madness seemed to strike our little town. Girls that had dated Germans were dragged from their homes to the main square, where a platform had been erected and these girls had their heads shaved in front of a mad crowd. Young men that had lived hiding in the woods all of a sudden appeared from nowhere. They were furious that while they were in hiding trying to serve their country these girls were siding with the enemy. It was a very bad experience which could have turned into a mild revolt, but for the FFI who restored order. The Allies of course did not get involved. This was not their problem; it was a personal and internal affair that the French people had to deal with. This kind of behavior did not just happen in our town, it went like wild fire throughtout our country.

Among this great confusion people started to get hold of themselves and try to rebuild what was needed as an emergency, but there were no machineries, no equipment of any kind. The Allies did their best to restore some bridges over the river on a temporary basis. Their equipment was coming in but very slowly. Only the emergency repairs were covered.

One point of interest was that the Germans and Italians prisoners were used to do the work.

Like a dream, a little at a time, everything came into focus. The Allies were extremely helpful. The Depot E-521 became a big family. Equipment and supplies were displayed on the grounds surrounding the main building which was the Headquarters and entirely reserved for Administrative offices. Other buildings started to be erected, shops for machinery, a special area for security and of course a large prefabricated building housing the Medical Department. Next to it another big construction became the kitchens, cafeteria, and Officers' Club. In no time we had a little town on our hands.

The special service organized entertainment for the military and the USO brought in bands and performers as well. One had to join the Club USO and they could attend the dances. They were furnished transportation because the club was located in Marseille. I attended the dances quite frequently, both at the Officers' Club as well as the big dances for the G.I.s which were held in the Cafeteria. However, my mother did not allow me to go unless I was properly chaperonned.

I became quite popular and loved every minute of it. Mother had resumed sewing but only for me for the time being, because I needed clothes desperately; fabrics were hard to find and we had to be resourceful.

On the business front, the French Government had allocated two Germans to work at the shop for free. This was to compensate my uncles for the loss they had suffered at the hands of the Germans; all their machinery gone to mention just a few of the losses. The Germans had to work along with my uncle by hand and it took a long time to accomplish anything. Pipo and Lino treated them decently. Both felt sorry for them, they had no family, had lost everything and they did not want to return to Germany. They had no choice then and very little now. They worked for my uncles an entire year. Fortunately Pipo and Lino managed to purchase various machines (second hand) which they were convinced were actually theirs but could not prove it.

It seemed like the bad days were over for us. The war was still taking its toll on the north of France and we prayed for the safekeeping of our soldiers. Nini was always in our mind; most of the time we did not know where he was. We had not heard from my father either, but that was not uncommon.

Photos from civilian office, Headquarters, and the Provost Marshal Office.

The Price of Freedom

Three months had flown by since the day I had started to work for the Allies and Christmas was now upon us. We had not celebrated any holidays, let alone Christmas, in years. But this year of 1944 was different. There was hope at the Engineer Depot 521 and many events were taking place. They had built a large tent and were getting ready for a Christmas celebration. I attended this party along with all of the civilian help. First, a non-denominational midnight service was held due to the various religions among the troops. Then the main officers in charge of the depot delivered their speeches, followed by a buffet where the food was magnificently arranged just like a picture and finally, a dance. Many soldiers were homesick and were singing their favorite songs, reminiscing on the past Christmases they had spent at home. There were tears and laughs and everyone agreed it was an unbelievable celebration.

Many lives were lost on the France/Germany border, the Battle of the Bulge raged and many people were worried about the fate of their relatives and friends. Toward the middle of January we received a call from my father. He seemed more worried than usual. He had not heard from Nini for over a month. I asked him if he had any further details on Nini's mission which I presumed was located in *Paris*. He told me he would come by train to talk to us because he was not at liberty to discuss this over the phone. He was on the *French Riviera* and would have to take the train to *Marseille* and then take the bus into *Marignane*. I had not seen my father for a very long time and we rarely spoke to him so when he said he was coming down in person to talk to us, this made me become very concerned and worried. I had that feeling like my stomach was coming up to my throat and I knew deep down, something was really wrong. All I can remember was thinking about Nini-praying to God to keep Nini safe.

Before his departure approximately a month ago, Nini had stopped in *Marseille* to visit my Aunt Honorine. He could not take the time to come to *Marignane* to see us. He was so proud of his American uniform that he had to show it to someone. That day, Henri, who was still always dressed in a disguise of some sort, had come to Aunt Honorine's house and tried to convince Nini to change his mind about his upcoming mission.

"Are you crazy?!" Henri retorted, "I almost died trying to get away from that!"

Nini replied, "But that was different. You were in a camp held as a prisoner and you could not help it. I have a choice and I intend to pursue that choice. If I die, it will be doing duty for my country and for the entire world. This I must do."

The Blue Ring

That was the last time any of my family saw or heard from him again.

Two days after his phone call, my father appeared at the house. He seemed extremely anxious. He proceeded to tell us what had happened since the *Pyrenées*. The FFI had moved him toward *St. Raphael* without telling him why. They must have known of the operation "Anvil" but he knew nothing about this. Nini of course went with him and ended up underground relaying messages, calculating distances and devising strategies which in the long run paid off and he became one of the leaders. If a mission looked difficult they would call Nini to do it since he had acquired a high reputation of succeeding in the toughest predicaments. Nini spoke perfect English, also spoke Italian and somehow managed to learn some German. He was charming, good-natured and was always optimistic even in the worst conditions. Along with all of these characteristics he was ingenious at what he did and this alone helped in the landing.

It seemed that during some transmissions from the "Maquis" he had captured valuable information that was sent by the enemy lines. My father did not know what the information was all about. All he knew was that Nini had to leave the camp and report the information he had intercepted to some higher authority. Thanks to Nini, the information turned out to be true and by bringing it to their attention, traps had been avoided and many lives were saved. After this, it was to no one's surprise that when the Americans landed on this little beach on the *Riviera*, Nini was the first to be contacted. They immediately furnished him with a uniform and enrolled him for some very important mission in *Paris*. My father was told that this mission was not very dangerous, but Nini was extremely excited and so proud that he was bursting.

That was the last time that my father saw Nini. This was in mid-November. Since then he had inquired about Nini everywhere he could, without any success. We finally tried to calm him down even though our hearts were heavy and all we could do was hope and pray. We tried to change the subject by questioning him on his work and his life and he then started to tell us his story.

He had been with the "Maquis" for a while and under the cover of the produce company he made their deliveries, which sometimes included secretly moving people. At one point it became very dangerous for him, so he decided to show the Germans or their collaborators that he was doing nothing wrong. He went and applied for a job to drive the German high-ranking officers to their destinations. He was hired and among other destinations he made frequent trips to Vichy (which was at that time the capital of southern France). My father would collect all kinds of information and pass it on to the "Maquis", actually Nini at the other end. Not only was he very good at it but he also had convinced the Germans that he was on their side. They began to let down their guard and began to talk more freely about what was going on. This was always in German of course. To my knowledge my father didn't speak German but sometimes the Germans would get carried away and brag a little in French to my father who would just smile and nod.

The Price of Freedom

Father continued to tell us how he had lost contact with all of his brothers and sister, having no idea where they were. On one of his trips to *Vichy* he was ordered to pick up an important delegate. While he was sitting in a limousine waiting and looking all around the area to catch any detail worth reporting, his eyes caught the silhouette of a man all dressed in a white expensive suit, with white shoes and an equally expensive white hat. Something was very familiar about the man. As the man dressed in white was coming down the steps in front of a magnificently architectural building, their eyes eventually met. For a brief instant there was shock in both of their eyes, immediately followed by indifference. My father knew at that moment that this was his lost brother Armando. To my father's surprise, his brother was not working for the FFI but for the Germans. For a second my father held his breath, not knowing what Armando was going to do after seeing him there. Fortunately his brother pretended he did not know him and saved my father from being discovered by the Germans.

He also was trying to protect himself; what would the Germans think if they knew both were working on opposite sides! Here was my father in a chauffeur uniform driving a limousine and there was Armando. obviously someone important in the eyes of the Germans. He told us of the shame he felt and how that moment had never left him. To think that he and Nini risked their lives everyday to help people, save their country and for humanity, while his brother Armando was now a traitor, all for money and power. To my knowledge this was the last time the two brothers saw each other. (Years later Armando did try to contact me from prison, where he definitely belonged).

After spending most of the afternoon with us my father left to catch his bus and train to go back to *St. Raphael* where he hoped to receive news on Nini. There was a lot of confusion behind the lines. Our family asked some French people what news they had received from the front. They responded by telling us it was extremely bad and possibly Nini just could not get hold of us. I even went to the extent of asking Major Shinn to find out some news on Nini. He tried to inquire about his whereabouts to no avail. Nini had just disappeared. We thought and hoped that perhaps part of his mission was to remain somewhere unknown. In the back of our minds we kept thinking that he was in *Paris*, the newly liberated city.

On that Monday morning, March 26, 1945, when I entered my office I was informed that the CEO wanted to see me in his office immediately. I had been working for the Allied Forces now for over six months, so I was a little perplexed as to why he wanted to see me. As I entered the CEO's office, I noticed that he was surrounded by several members of his staff which included the doctor, Captain Devereau and of all people, my Uncle Lino! My two uncles had worked for the Allied Forces for several months setting up the carpentry section but were now back to running their own carpentry shop. There was no reason for Lino to be there since he no longer worked for them. The only reason for him to be there was if a catastrophe had happened. My legs felt like rubber and after I took in the ambiance of this setting with everyone's seriousness and their silence, I had this terrible feeling in the pit of my stomach. I immediately thought something had happened to my mother, whom I had just left thirty minutes before. I must have said so aloud because my Uncle Lino, unable to speak, just shook his head "no" and handed me a blue piece of paper which was a telegram.

With trembling fingers I picked it up and stared at it, not being able to comprehend. The words were dancing before my eyes making no sense at all. When I finally was able to digest the meaning of the words in front of me, the entire impact hit me so hard that I lost my balance.

Immediately someone grabbed me and led me to a chair. A feeling of anger, disbelief and anguish at once overcame me. In the telgram the War Department was informing us that my brother Nini had been killed in action on December 11, 1944.

I was in shock. The major offered to call the War Department immediately to see where this had happened. While his aides were busy calling around I got up from the chair and was staring out the window, tears streaming down my checks, still not believing. This could not happen. Not now Dear God! Like a movie, I relived the past. Nini and I at the kitchen table in *Menton* planning the future, Nini and I delivering propaganda papers, Nini and I trying to find wood under the snow in the *Pyrenees* Mountains to light a fire, the bitter cold we suffered and the millions of things we had planned to do. This was all over. I would never see or talk to him again! Here I thought he was indestructible! All of these years, the hardships, the hope, and the faith were all gone now! Nothing remained. We had been cheated!! The news of Nini's death was the most horrific nightmare to me. Only it was not a nightmare, it was reality.

As I stood there deep in my thoughts and numb, I suddenly realized someone was talking to me. It was my Uncle Lino. He was trying to explain how the telegram had arrived at the house on Saturday and how he had intercepted it, not knowing how to approach me first before seeing my mother. He had decided that he would wait and approach me at the office on Monday. Thinking back I can recall how strange he had acted during the entire weekend. Pulling myself together, hardly able to stand up, my uncle and I walked out of the office to face the ordeal, the first being to tell my mother the horrific news: Nini had been killed.

Although the war was so close to ending, I felt that it had just begun. Since Nini's death the war has never really ended for me.

. . .

The death of my brother Nini caused our family to despair with devastating shock and sorrow. My mother's health from then on kept deteriorating. She was despondent and severely ill. For the next month we did not know if she was going to survive. I was beside myself and as it often happens, I expected another disaster to occur. My fear was that I would lose my mother also.

The Price of Freedom

After lots of care, plenty of help from friends and relatives, my mother started to get better and eventually was back on her feet, but it took a long time.

As if peace was not ours to have, I returned home one evening, extremely exhausted and sick and went directly to bed. Later on in the evening I decided to get up and simply passed out. The doctor was summoned once more, this time on my behalf. His diagnosis was frightening: Scarlet Fever. Immediately my Uncle Pipo worried how he could work at his shop and keep his family from catching it. Fortunately they were now residing in town. My other uncle, Lino, decided to remain and help. We were put in quarantine, signs posted at our gate. I assume I was between life and death for many days. At one point I even became unconscious and the doctor suggested to my mother that she should advise my father of my condition because I may not make it. With all the deprivations and stress my immune system was extremely weak. The doctor came over every day, sometimes twice a day. There were no hospitals in *Marignane* and I could not be moved to *Marseille* where the facilities were more adequate. No one could take a chance of an epidemic.

Uncle Lino proceeded to track my father down and finally reached him and talked to him. My father was still trying to come to grips with the loss of Nini but he indicated that he would come. He never did. He never even called to check on me.

I burned with fever for days. My skin peeled. My hair became thin, but somehow I survived. God must have had some other plans for me. I had my hair cut short. The doctor gave me a homemade potion that strengthened my hair and made it grow.

Every day during my sickness it was very rare not to find some kind of package from the Depot left by the gate. Sometimes it was canned food. I also received sweets, small bars of chocolate, K-rations and even medication, which was shown to the doctor. He would administer the medicine to me, giving me immense relief. Medications as well as food, were still scarce. Also newspapers were delivered with greetings from all the gang, people I never heard of before. These newspapers were American, and carried "Dagwood" in the comics section.

During my convalescence period I reproduced many of the characters from the Dagwood family "free hand" and applied them to a special circumstance connected with the person I was sending them to as a thank-you card. I had received so many notes, cards and little gifts that it took me days to thank everyone with my drawings. Many officers and soldiers as well, with whom I dealt frequently in my job, had become very friendly and they were forever teasing me, calling me "Blondie." I drew pictures of Dagwood and Blondie in certain events that had happened in the past and Blondie would always tell them "Thank you" at the end. I mailed them to each and every one, never the same drawing, nor the same event. It did help me tremendously, mentally and physically.

By then close to three months after my sickness and six months into the mourning of my brother had gone by. When I finally returned to work I received an incredible welcome and picked up where I had left off.

Every morning Major Shinn held a coffee break in his office. All the officers attended and I used to think that it was a nice friendly way for Major Shinn to keep in touch with his staff and the current events.

The first day of my return I was asked to please join them for the coffee break at 10:00 a.m. I was very happy for the invitation and at 10:00 a.m. sharp I entered the office to a standing ovation. I was embarrassed and flattered at the same time. They had all missed me and were truly glad to see me. That was repeated over and over. One of the officers handed me a cup of coffee and asked if I needed sugar and cream. As I started to answer him I noticed the walls and almost dropped my cup. The walls were entirely covered with my thank-you notes, my drawings of Dagwood and family, including Blondie. Some even suggested I should apply for a job with Walt Disney. I had to fight away the tears that sprang into my eyes. This was really like returning to my family.

From then on I was in attendance at the coffee breaks and eventually took over the duties that it involved, ordering coffee or tea and some rolls from the mess hall, displaying it nicely, even doing the pouring. They all agreed it made them feel at home.

I was invited by several gentlemen to the Officer's Club dances but had to decline. I later explained to Major Shinn that our customs required for a person in mourning to wear black for the first few months, then grey, then white for an entire year and also I should not attend dances, etc. He understood and must have passed the word around. I began to be invited to picnics, outdoor games, and trips on the canals, which were acceptable.

The Provost Marshall took us, three girlfriends of mine and myself, on a picnic on a barge while floating on the canal which connected to the sea. We had a wonderful time, compliments of our host a very nice and good-looking gentleman. That trip was to become the first of many outings.

Meanwhile the equipment located on Engineer Depot E- 521 was being sold or allocated to various projects at an incredible speed, decreasing the need for civilian help. Our staff was reduced by more than half. The civilian quarters that had been put together in a type of warehouse were no longer needed. Except for a few foremen and their crew who were to remain in the previous area, the administration was moved into the main building. The offices were more comfortable and in addition to my regular duties, I was to direct the customers (all army) to the proper zones. These were sections where a certain type of requested material was located. But first I had to check their credentials carefully.

During my absence, Major Shinn had brought back an assistant he used to have in Belgium. He had recently been in charge of restoring the lighting system on the pier and harbor of Marseille. Since this task had been accomplished, he was resuming his duties at the E-521. His name was Merritt Darr. I had met him as well as many others who were often around Major Shinn. Actually the major had introduced Merritt to me twice as his "right arm."

Then smiling, he had told him, "I believe you have become my left arm. Miss Vella is my right arm now." From the look on Merritt's face he did not care one way or another. I don't believe he even heard what was said. He just looked at me and grinned. He looked just like a kid with beautiful brown eyes and a great smile. He was very tall and slender. I returned the smile.

I was extremely impressed, but had found myself in this situation before, so I didn't give it another thought. I did notice Major Shinn's look. He was trying to play "Cupid."

Headquarters.

Merritt

It seemed that Major Shinn was very fond of Merritt and there was no doubt in my mind he had a certain respect for me. The man was very understanding, considerate, yet he was strict and ran the depot with an iron hand. Like anyone in authority, he was disliked by some of the men, but at all times he was fair and concerned about the welfare of any person without descrimination.

Merritt made a habit of coming to see me every day, asking for the location of a certain type of material and each time it was something different. At first I thought Major Shinn was trying to check on me, wanting to know how well I knew my business, since these were new duties to which I had been assigned.

One day I asked Merritt point blank, "Being an aide to the Commander in Chief, shouldn't you know where all the equipment is located?" He grinned and replied, "Most of the time I should, but I like your accent and that gives me a chance to talk with you." I didn't want to encourage him, so I smiled and switched to business.

Merrit Darr

He was not the first one to come and ask questions (of which they knew the answers) or just come to say hello or ask me out. I was flattered and was always nice to them. Being reserved as I was seemed to be very intriguing to outgoing types, like I assumed Americans were. I was also trying very hard to improve my English, I should say my British English which had to be adapted to American English. I did not know American slang, making me the object of laughter when I asked questions relating to it. I must confess I enjoyed enormously being the center of attention.

My mother gave me a watch for my birthday, the only one she had been able to find based on average price and availability. It had a red band. The watch was pretty but the band had to go.

The next day I decided to wear it to the office. When Merritt came to see me he noticed the watch with the red band. (I had been wearing black, then grey, then white for the mourning.) Politely he asked, "Is this new?" I replied, "I got this for my birthday." He looked at the watch again and bluntly said, "I don't like the band." "Neither do I," I answered. So he continued, "You know, I have an idea. I have to go to *Marseille* to check the pier and harbor. Why don't you let me have your watch and I will get you a decent band." I hesitated, not knowing him that well. This was my first watch and I had very few possessions. Besides, I had worn it less than a couple of hours. But my reluctance was short-lived. I simply unfastened my watch and handed it to him. "I'll bring it back tomorrow," he said and was gone. I nodded, all the time thinking about my mother's reactions when I got home.

Sure enough, when I came in she noticed the watch was missing. "Where is your watch?" she said. I acted casually and told her: " I did not like the band, so bright red and this nice American who is Major Shinn's aide made the same remark and offered to get me another band in Marseille, he will bring it back tomorrow." She said, "I believe you have just lost your watch." I disagreed, but decided not to say so. I hoped she was wrong. The next day I waited anxiously for Merritt but he did not show up. When I came home that night things were a little tense as my mother said, "I told you, didn't I?" There was nothing I could add and I kept hoping there was an explanation for it. The same thing occurred the following day. No Merritt and no watch. All day I was preoccupied. I was beginning to have second thoughts. On the third day Merritt arrived with my watch, which now had a beautiful expandable band. He handed it to me saying, "This is your birthday present from me. It took longer than I thought to get my business taken care of. I was going to call you but I knew you would understand." How little did he know! I was so relieved I couldn't wait to get home and show my mother. I thanked him and proceeded to tell him I could not accept such a gift from him and I wanted to reimburse him for the band. However he was so insistent that I finally gave up and thanked him graciously.

When I walked into the house that night, I was very proud of myself and told my mother, "You see, I told you I trusted him. The watch band is a gift for my birthday." Mother and I discussed whether I should accept a present like that and she admitted that she had given up ever seeing my watch again. I said to her, "Mother, you have little faith in people," to which she replied, "I have learned the hard way."

From then on Merritt was a permanent fixture at work whenever he was in town. He would come and see me, sometimes twice a day, without using any excuse and if I didn't see him I would wonder where he was. Sometimes, returning from his trips, he would bring me a little trinket.

One day he asked, "I heard you and your friends had a great time last Sunday on a picnic." "Yes," I replied, "The Captain was so nice. We did have a great time."

The following weekend was around the corner. "Do you have a plan for this weekend?" he inquired. "Not yet," I said, "I should probably stay home and get some work caught up." He went on his way saying, "See you later," and it was not very long before he was back. "How would you like to go with your friends for a drive along the beaches, like *Carry-le-Rouet, Carro*, and a lot of little towns along the way? I will bring a picnic for all of us and we will have a great day." After checking with my friends and my mother of course, we agreed. I explained that my mother thought I was too young and the only way I was allowed to go out was with friends, telling her when she was to expect me to return and where I was going. Merritt thought that was great. He approved of the rules.

On Sunday morning my friends had come to the house, this being the first time and Merritt met everyone: Marie, Elise and Renee, as well as my mother.

Marie was the niece of the Pilias', owners of the grocery store, the ones that had been so nice to me, during the food distributions. She and I had become friends while trying to help her uncles' business during those hard times. She still worked at the store. Elise's parents owned the *Bar-Tabacs*, a business where they sold liquor, newspapers, stamps, post cards, all kinds of pipes as well as tobacco, cigarettes and cigars. Elise ran the counter on the Tabacs' side of the establishment. Renee was the daughter a very wealthy rancher. He owned an impressive amount of land and Renee helped him with the books and the running of his business

I was the only one who worked for the Allies.

It was agreed that Merritt was to bring me home first before he dropped off the other girls. He really wanted to make my mother happy and she was delighted. He even said his father would approve of these rules and he was going to mention it to him regarding his younger sister.

Thus began a wonderful period of discovering our neighboring towns, enjoying our freedom and appreciating every minute of it.

As I came out of my period of mourning I started to attend the Special Service dances and Officer's Club parties at the Depot E-521, always escorted by my friends. They were enjoying the dances tremendously as well as the various sightseeing trips. For me it was all new but for them it was like picking up the pieces.

After the dances sometimes we would drive by a rotating bridge crossing a large canal leading to the sea. It was beautiful at night. The street lighting had been restored. With no more curfew we were living again. Lots of G.I.'s were on the bridge with their girlfriends. I remember one of them throwing a flashlight which was turned on just to check and see how long it would last down in the water. We watched the little light for a long time, thinking to ourselves someone must have had too much to drink, when Merritt made the comment aloud.

All the barracks in the depot lodging the G.I.'s were named after famous prisons, such as Alcatraz, Sing-Sing, etc. At times I wondered if they felt like they should act the part! The M.P.'s were kept busy according to my reports.

Whether we went on outings or to the dances, Merritt would pick up the girls at an agreed spot, usually in front of the *Bar Tabacs*, then come and pick me up to take us to whatever was planned. He was the most considerate young man. I believe in a way we both learned to dance together. I had never heard of the jitterbug and he had not heard of waltzes and tangos. The band played only slow dances or wild jitterbug. We had a wonderful time. I still can see us on the dance floor, dancing to the music of "Sentimental Journey" (which became one of our songs), "I'll Walk Alone," "More," "I Wish I Knew," "Dream," "Candy," "In The Mood," and many, many more, until we came to

"Good Night Ladies." This is how Merritt and I fell in love.

One particular evening he was supposed to pick us up for a dance and I became ill. I had some type of chest cold so I cancelled by calling him and also the girls. Everyone was disappointed, including me. I was in bed with a fever and feeling sorry for myself when a vehicle came into our courtyard, the headlights shining into our windows. I told my mother not to respond because I did not expect anyone and my Uncle Lino was not at home. Someone was being persistent. My mother finally went out. She did not speak English and Merritt, the caller, did not speak French. They managed to communicate with sign language and the car left. My mother locked the door and was getting ready to go to bed when the car came back. This time she did not hesitate, assuming it was Merritt again. She was right. He had gone to the Depot infirmary and bought aspirin, some kind of rubbing lotion for the chest, cough drops and juices. He talked without stopping, telling my mother how to use whatever he had brought and my mother was talking also, each in their own language. She had left the bedroom door open and I could hear some of it through the hallway. I could not help thinking this was extremely funny and when she came in with a large bag and a look of frustration on her face we both burst out laughing. Again I told her, "Didn't I tell you he was nice and considerate?"

The next day everyone who came to the shop had to hear about Merritt. He became an instant hero.

Merritt decided to come around for no reason in particular just to say hello to my uncles. He would go into the shop and try to visit with them. Of course he made sure I was nearby most of the time, like on weekends; the sign language could only go so far.

He supervised a group of Germans, some of whom were involved in woodwork, so whenever he could, he would ask all kinds of questions and I would translate for him. I even had to help him write it down. Pipo was so thrilled, he loved his work and wanted everyone else to do the same. He would get carried away and talked a mile a minute; whenever he was excited he would switch from French to Italian. It did not make any difference with Merritt because he did not understand either one.

On occasion some of the officers wanting a certain type of furniture made at the Depot by the Germans prisoners, after talking with Merritt, would come to my uncles who would design it to their specifications in blueprint. Everyone would get what they wanted and all were happy.

Eventually we knew this state of euphoria was not going to last forever. There were rumors that an agreement between the American and the French Governments was upcoming.

Merritt started to get worried about being transferred and decided that he should get some commitment from me. He asked me to marry him; with me being a minor, he also consulted my family. They liked him very much, however they tried to make him understand that because of my age it would be better to postpone it. They did not like the idea of me as a "war bride". They also thought that once he was back home he would see things their ways. However he assured them that he would wait and he would return...

The End Of An Era

The Engineer Depot E-521 had been in existance for over two years, when as expected, an agreement between the American and the French Governments was finalized. This would mean a tremendous change in the way the surplus was being handled.

Major Shinn called me in his office and wanted to know if I would be interested going to work for the United Nations in New York. He explained he could easily arrange all of the necessary details. He even went so far as to go visit my family and took Dr. Devereau with him to translate. My family thanked the Major profusely but declined and I had to admit they were right; I could not leave at that point in time.

Therefore the Major did the next best thing: He strongly recommended me to the French Military Officials and I became manager in charge of the civilian division of the depot under the French Government when they took over October 26, 1946.

During the ceremonies of the transference of leadership I was officially introduced to the top executives of the French Military by Major Shinn. At the same time, the American Flag came down to be replaced by the French one. Officials of both countries, surrounded by troops, performed a very emotional ceremony, which was attended by former employees as well as crowds from the neighboring towns. It was their way to thank the Allies for all their help and many shed a tear or two. As it often happens in those circumstances, it brought back memories of the sacrifice of young men. The speech given in both languages was extremely stirring.

Shortly thereafter the Allied Forces were transferred to Germany and Belgium where unfinished business awaited them.

Merritt was transferred to Germany. We were all so sad when he came home to tell everyone goodbye. I did not know if I would ever see him again but he kept telling me he would come back.

This was the end of an era...

From then on the depot became known as *"Depot de Surplus Americain"*.

Upon my transfer my first duty was to hire civilian personnel. I found it ironic. This was the way I had started with Major Shinn. Officers in charge were mostly of aristocratic descent "Blue blood". A new reorganization was underway. The depot of surplus was comprised of every imaginable type of machinery such as industrial, agricultural, construction equipment and much more. Buildings, roads, bridges, railroads, airports, everything that had been destroyed in our entire country had to be replaced, rebuilt. Fields had to be restored to production, water had to be made available for public consumption as well as for irrigation; on a larger scale, livestock had to be planned anew.

It was a monstrous job and it took a lot of planning but we never forgot that it had been made possible thanks to the United States of America.

The entire Depot inventory as well as all the records were in English. An urgent need for translators was imperative. Overnight my work had taken a different turn.

I had hired Raymonde once more, among the many people that were now part of the new depot. At first we were so involved with our job we could hardly breathe. I missed Merritt; he kept writing almost everyday and I wrote back as much as I could but the new reorganization was extremely demanding. I realized that American ways seemed a lot simpler to handle, whereas the French, especially the military, had an unbelievable amount of paperwork. Every type of merchandise transferred required a "requisition" which was written on four or five copies, each going to several departments; sometimes the merchandise was not worth the paper itself. There was so much to do, we just had to get organized in some way.

Then, Merritt now located in Belgium wrote that he was being released; he intended to come to France to visit me before going to America. Sooner than I expected, there he was, and again expressed his wish to marry me. He had barely been away a few months and again my family refused, offering the same excuses as before.

I understood if I left, my mother would be all alone. She was still having a hard time accepting the loss of my brother. I just could not leave her at this time. Once again Merritt promised he would return.

However I knew deep down this was an impossible dream. I had to make an inventory of my life. Raymonde who had survived her share of heartbreak told me that I had to start going out; all work no play did not sound good at all. If it was meant to be, it would happen. In the meantime we had learned how short life could be and had to take advantage of any possibilities of happiness

This is when we started to go out, first just out of boredom. Dancing was now a new way of life. There were "Thé dansant" which was dancing to the sound of a combo at tea time, usually on Sunday afternoon; and Ballroom dancing Friday and Saturday nights, a very popular time to go out, meet friends and dance.

Mardi Gras, in the past, had been a very big celebration. Bal Masques would take place on Sunday night followed by a parade on Tuesday. One evening Raymonde arrived at my house out of breath, "Marie-Jeanne, do you know there is going to be a masquerade ball?" she said . "I hadn't heard" I replied, "But what I would really like is to be on a float in the parade." My mother who had been very concerned about my lack of enthusiasm and was taking everything in, suddenly said "What would you wear? If you have any idea we probably could whip something up." We both were ecstatic! We started to think what we could be and what we could use for material. My mother said "Do you remember the torn parachutes that the Americans had given you?" Suddenly I remembered. Parachutes were made of silk, the color was a

light shade of grey but we could dye them. All excited we started to plan; we also contacted the officials in charge of the parade but because we had nothing to show them we were turned down. Raymonde was easily convinced but not I, there had to be a way. In the meantime, since we could not be on the float, we may as well plan for the Masquerade Ball. This was Wednesday and the three of us planned to spend the night sewing. We were going to be fairies "Fées". We made the dresses that night; the next day we ordered some stars made in aluminum, with a pin hole drilled into them in order to be able to sew them on. Once the dresses were finished, my mother dyed them; I wanted mine blue and Raymonde chose peach. The next night we sewed the stars on. We worked feverishly in our spare time and by Sunday night we were ready. Earlier Saturday morning I had contacted the parade official again telling him that our costumes were finished and explaining what they looked like. He rather impatiently said "I would have to see them before I could give you an answer" and abruptly added, "But the way you describe them, I don't think so" and turned away, leaving me very disappointed.

Raymonde was dating an officer from the depot, one of the blue blood; my escort was Pierre, a nice guy in the Air Force. We told them we would see them at the Ball. Raymonde's boyfriend had to decline as he could not go due to some military rules, but Pierre was going to meet me there. We did not mention anything about our disguise. We waited until the ball was well under way to show up. We were masked and we looked very nice, We had changed our hair, wrapped around a crown, wore long gloves up to the elbow and with our dresses floor length covered all over with lots of glitter, it was really hard to know us. We were about the same size. We danced with everybody all night and we were a great success. I could see Pierre watching the door waiting for me to arrive. I felt guilty but did not go near him. I was having the time of my life. I did not talk of course and my smile was covered by my blue mask. Everyone was wondering who we were; they would call us by various names to see our reaction but we would shake our heads "No".

Around midnight we knew we had to leave because at the sound of 12 o'clock everyone was to take their mask off. By that time I knew I did not want anyone to know who I was, especially with Pierre looking very unhappy and for some reason Raymonde didn't either. So we tried to leave by the back door but the committee was watching and they objected. I finally spoke to one of the group and told them it was a very serious matter and we had to go, but to no avail. Of course in doing so, they knew who I was; I had given myself away. I really wanted to leave. Later we pretended to go to the ladies room, then snuck into the kitchen of the establishment, but again, they had outguessed us and we had to return to the ballroom. We went into a corner hoping we would be able to remove the mask and leave but the next thing I knew someone was talking on the microphone and two officials approched me and ask me to follow them. I was led to the stage. I did try to protest but could see there was no way out. I had been chosen to be the " Queen of the Mardi Gras".

What a shock that was. Under a thunder of applause I came down, from the stage to face my astounded friend. Well he was far from being thrilled and I felt guilty but since the dancing resumed we danced in silence. That did not last long as I had become extremely popular lately and tonight everyone was surrounding me and cutting in.

We had planned for Raymonde to stay at my home and we arrived in the early hours of the morning, exhausted, lauded with small gifts, flowers, and instructions for the parade. My mother was up to check the commotion and was really happy for us. We then tried to get some well needed sleep. The next two days were a holiday; we spent Monday recuperating and getting ready for the parade. On Tuesday morning the parade officials sent a car for us Raymonde was to be my-lady-in-waiting; we were taken to the main float. The official who had turned us down was there with the welcoming committee and the look on his face was a small victory in itself but we were so happy, we did not hold it against him. On the parade route, crowded endlessly, Pierre was among the crowd holding a bunch of red roses and managed to hand them to me (he had recovered).

This was the beginning of a very busy social life. I was asked to participate in many events. I became quite in demand: representing achievements by women, congratulating winners at soccer games (called football in France).

A few months later I was informed that I had been automatically entered into the contest to run for the title Miss Marseille-Marignane. This usually took place before the "football season" started. They had many dances to raise funds and at one of those dances they were going to announce the winner. I really was not too excited about it I had too much to do. Once was enough but because I was still on my reign of "Queen of the Mardi Gras" I graciously agreed to be part of it

My mother again came around with some kind of gauze material, dyed this time in pink and decorated with gold butterflies. I went through all the requirements; the result was not to be announced until Saturday night at a formal dance which was held the day before the first game of the series. To my greatest surprise I was voted "Miss Marseille-Marignane". Thus began a year of madness. I believe this frenzy was caused by all the years of deprivation; we had bottled up our fears and emotions and it was like letting off steam. I was part of all the inaugurations, ribbon cuttings, dedicating buildings. I was ask to model for stores at special gatherings, visited schools, and an endless amount of duties. I was constantly on the go and had to admit that I enjoyed it tremendously.

However something was lacking. Recently I had noticed that Merritt had stopped writing entirely. I had already assumed that this was going to happen but nevertheless I was terribly hurt. Even thought Merritt was out of my life I still could not get him off my mind entirely. Perhaps being busy was what I needed.

Our airport had been reconstructed and it had taken forever. They were in the process of making it an International Airport but for the time being it only serviced Europe and North Africa. Thanks to this project our town was getting travelers staying overnight. We had two hotels in town but the main one was l'Hotel Moderne and that was where our dancing parties were being held.

Sometimes planes would remain overnight in Marignane; the pilots would then stay at the hotel and come to the ballroom for a drink. At one of these occasions I met Charles. He was with Air France and came through our town often. We started to meet occasionally and whenever he was in town coming even for a short stop, he would call first; then if I was available, would send a car to pick me up. We would meet in the pilots lounge, drink coffee and visit for a while, then the car would take me back. At other times I would meet other pilots and radio navigators and we would talk, dance, and just be friendly. Yves and Robert were some of these casual acquaintances. I saw them several times and did not think anything of it. But they must of thought otherwise. Whenever they were in Marignane they would contact me by way of the airport swichboard and ask me out for a drink. Yves was with Tri-Star, Robert with Air-Algeria. They did not know each other. Then one Sunday I went to a "The Dansant" (from 3:00 to 7:00 p.m.) The weather was very bad, planes were detoured and I was about to leave for home when my mother called. She was furious. She reported that there were three small vans all parked around our villa and the phone had been ringing incessantly. Would I mind getting home and straighten out this mess. That I did. What had happened was that because of the weather all three planes had been grounded and the pilots and navigator were staying at the same hotel. In the bar they started to talk and decided to call a girl they had met and this girl happened to be me. That night I really got in trouble all the way around. I was not dating any of them, just being friendly. My family never let me forget the commotion caused by this state of affairs. It was the talk of the town for a while. I had many problems that way, the less I was interested the more in demand I became. My mother strangely enough had encouraged me to go out on dates and by the same token, she was always asking all kind of questions if I went out with someone more than twice. Was this serious? She seemed to be overly worried when I did not show any interest in anyone.

Meanwhile at work the French government was doing a great job at dispatching the equipment to the people needing it to rebuild our country and after 3-1/2 years (we were nearing 1950) the Depot closed its doors for good.

The *Foire Internationale de Marseille*, associated indirectly with embassies from all over the world through a special foreign service, offered me a job which consisted of contacting each one individually and inviting them to attend our Technical-Commercial Exposition.

I became head of the Foreign Service Department and was trusted with all kinds of social duties whenever some celebrities were in town. I was the Hostess with the welcoming committee for all English-speaking and Italian-speaking personalities; knowing their language and customs, I made all arrangements with the help of two secretaries.

Quite often we would have movie stars filming in the area. They would be invited to the *"Foire de Marseille"*. I would then be the official hostess and

would escort them to the various radio stations and in particular to *"Radio Monte Carlo"*, which was broadcasting directly from the *Parc Chanot in Marseille*, during the Exhibition. Everyday a special event was taking place honoring a different country followed by a reception for our guests of honor. On such occasion I was always in charge.

I used to take a bus to *Marseille* every morning and return late at night. I never saw daylight in *Marignane*, except for Sundays and when closer to the *"Exposition"* not even then. My mother had resumed her profession and was kept busy sewing for clients.

One day, having completed my work at the office of the *Foire de Marseille* located at *La Canebiere*, the main artery of *Marseille,* I was told to take the afternoon off. The bus left regularly from the *Place de la Bourse* (which was the center of the city where the stock market was located). The buses were strictly for government people going directly to the airport and passed just in front of our home. I was given a special pass and could take any of them at any time. I was fortunate that the noon bus was late so when it did come, I boarded it and about 45 minutes later I was getting off in front of the shop. As I alighted from the bus I ran into the mailman. "Miss Vella," he said, "what a pleasure to see you. You are not here much and we miss you." He said this while sorting through his stack of mail. He finally pulled out one letter, say-

With Glen Ford at the "Foire de Marseille".

ing, "This is all you have for today. "Mon Dieu! you sure receive a lot of American mail." Naturally, I was speechless. When I recovered some I asked: "How long have you been on this route?" He replied: "Oh I have been on this route for years, and I could tell you pretty close how many letters you have received in the last year. I have a wonderful memory." He kept on divulging all his qualities as a postman. Holding the letter I walked into the house biting my lip and slamming the door with anger. My mother came running to the door to see what was happening and my Uncle Pipo came out of the shop concerned. After he had moved to town with his family, I didn't get to see him very much because I always came home late. I faced them both and asked, "Who gave you the right to hide my mail?"

They were confounded. Uncle Pipo started to scratch his head and looked at my mother for an explanation. So did I. She started to tell me she had lost one son and did not want to lose the only child she had left because this was what would happen if I went to America. We did have a serious discussion. Then without a word, my mother went back to the spare bedroom and came out with three shoe-boxes full of unopened letters from Merritt; a 2 to 3- year supply of letters.

The atmosphere in the house was rather stormy. I spent that afternoon going through some of the letters. I did not know what to do. I had to write Merritt and tell him what?

A couple of weeks later I received a summons from the mayor of Marignane who wanted to talk to me. This was strange and perplexing.

When I reported to the city hall and spoke to the mayor he informed me that Merritt Darr had requested a search with the Geneva Red Cross to find out my whereabouts. It seemed this was not the first time the mayor had contacted my family. This time however, he decided to do it officially. A summons would get me to show up at city hall. I was extremely embarrassed, more so when he added, "Marie-Jeanne, this gentleman has been writing to you for the

MINISTÈRE DES TRAVAUX PUBLICS ET DES TRANSPORTS

Secrétariat Général à l'Aviation Civile et Commerciale

Aéroport Principal de Marseille-Marignane

CARTE D'ADMISSION

PRIORITAIRE

dans les véhicules du SGACC N° 1812-

Nom Mademoiselle VELLA

Prénoms Marie Jeanne.

Service Direct.

Valable du 1er Janv. au 31 Déc. 1952

Le Titulaire,
(Signature)

Le Commandant
de l'Aéroport,
(Signature)

Bus pass.

longest time and to us also and you have not responded. Give this poor man at least a reason for avoiding his contact with you because he is driving our office nuts." I meekly apologized for any trouble this may have caused their office. Not wanting to confess my family's meddling in this I told the mayor that I had received a first letter just a few days ago but had never received any other letters before this and I had responded immediately.

Indeed, that fateful afternoon, after reading a large amount of the letters, I wrote Merritt. I did not know what to tell him so my letter was very flat.

I did mention that I had received a letter, not wanting to involve my family and told him this was the first; it was the truth. It was very hard to explain, so I told him about my new job; how I was always in Marseille, commuting back and forth, not having much time to myself.

France has always been plagued with srtikes in all types of businesses, still does. I hoped that he would consider the possibility. From then on we started to write to each other, like one writes to a pal.

After several exchanges we started to write about the past. Merritt mentioned that if he had to do it again, he would not have left when he did, without some kind of commitment from me.

Finally he told me he was thinking seriously about coming to visit me. I did not realize how serious he was, until he had set a date.

This was 1953 and the coronation of the Queen of England was going to take place.

"La Cauelrére" Marseille going to work.

Therefore Merritt, determined to see me in person once again, boarded the "Queen Elizabeth" to propose to me for the third time. Although my family was still against the idea of my move to the U.S.A., I accepted. Unfortunately I had to obtain a visa in addition to a passport and the visa was subject to a quota. Only so many people could enter the U.S.A. per year. We met with the American Consul as well as French Authorities and were informed that it would require around two years in order to clear the red tape. They even investigated my grandmother in Italy. A medical checkup, as well as dental, a knowledge of the English language and a good personal record were all part of the requirements. Merritt spent a couple of weeks with us trying to get the paper work taken care of and also getting re-acquainted. We were invited to several dinner parties, met many people, friends and relatives and finally Merritt returned to the States while I remained in *Marignane* and continued working at the *Foire Internationale de Marseille*.

New Life in America

The next two years had been very much the same as it had been before Merritt's visit. I was extremely busy with my work and had many social obligations quite demanding. However it was entirely different. I was no longer in limbo; I knew what I was going to do. In addition I had to plan our move, mine to the States and my mother's to her family home in Italy, this I told her until she could join me.

As it was customary, one had to have a trousseau when getting married. Because of the circumstances, my trousseau would be limited to clothes for the bride for all occasions.

The tradition requires that the parents of the bride furnish the kitchen essentials, while the parents of the groom would take care of the bedroom furnishing. This did not apply to me.

My family was very involved in the *"haute couture"* so everyone joined forces with my mother and went to work using their talents. Before long I had an unbelievable wardrobe with the latest designs.

Finally I was granted my visa and was to leave from *Cannes, France* onboard the "Independence" on the 12th of August. I will not deny that as the time came close I was getting rather nervous and I could see my family still had mixed feelings.

Before my departure mother and I moved to my Aunt Zize in Antibes. All her belongings had been moved to Perinaldo and mine were waiting to be shipped with me. Tante Zize had a shop on a prime location where she catered to the tourists from all over the world. Her shop had all kinds of foods for all nationalities and beliefs. While awaiting my departure I helped her using my knowledge of languages in her shop.

The fact that everyone knew that I was leaving created a lot of commotion. In the mist of that my aunt would just heave a sigh. They all gave advice and opinions. With all kinds of good wishes and many relatives, I was driven to Cannes where I boarded the ship. My mother and my aunt had chosen not to accompany me. We said good-bye in private. Neither were happy about my departure and I was beginning to get a feeling of guilt.

Once onboard the ship everyone tried to make you feel wonderful. I stayed on the deck as long as I could, looking at the lights of Cannes receding along the coast. I was pretty sad at that moment.

I followed the instructions and reached the dining room, where everyone felt the same as I did. Later the Captain asked if I would do him the honor to dance with him. It was the customary opening of the festivities, a ritual that took place every night; then he would go back to his running of the ship. Once the first dance was over, he would introduce me to some of his officers. We would then dance and talk for the rest of the evening, This happened several times. I believe I opened the ball with the captain three or four times and by then I knew several officers so time went very fast.

I had never been on the water before, let alone on a ship.

The crossing of the Atlantic Ocean lasted seven days more or less. The beginning of this book dealt with my arrival in New York and my first impressions so I will skip this part altogether.

Once in Alva, I settled at the residence of Merritt's parents and shared a room with Rosie, their younger daughter.

Immediately Rosie proceeded to introduce me to life in America.

From the beginning she was fascinated with my clothes, asking innumerable questions about everything under the sun; comparing, wondering why things were done differently and in a way she restored my self-confidence. I was not the only one unaware of the way of life in other countries.

I explained why my country, *France*, was according to American opinion, "behind". The destruction suffered during six years of war and occupation was not easily restored.

It would take many years to simply replace what had been lost. Our aim was to rebuild homes, bridges, airports, railroad stations, canals, schools, restore our fields and simply reconstruct our lives. We were interested in a basic living before we would worry about comfort and luxury. There was no comparison.

However as I was trying to explain what our goals were, I realized I could just talk my head off and none of these people would be able to understand what we went through; our losses, our hopes. They had no idea what went on in Europe; only the soldiers that had come to liberate us knew, to a certain extent.

I was introduced to all the American novelties: drive in theaters, fast foods, in particular the A&W Drive-In. I was amazed that in both instances one never got out of the car. I was making mental notes of what I needed to learn first and came to the conclusion that driving was going to be my first priority. One could not survive in America without cars. They were part of every phase of life, besides transportation.

Coffee breaks at mid-morning to the local "Drug Store" were evidently another American custom. I enjoyed them tremendeously. Not only the girls would show up and I met many of them, but the guys also would make a brief appearance and it would turn into a merry occasion. I became very popular, whether it was based on curiosity or plain kindness it didn't matter, it was fun. Even Merritt made a few appearances whenever he could after Rosie had mentioned my popularity.

Merritt was very proud of me, of course, but what surprised me most, was the way his parents paraded me in town, introducing me everywhere, to their friends as well as their acquaintances in the business world.

Jack, Merritt's father, was always up very early; I was an early riser myself and after a period of adjustment to time zone changes I would meet him every morning for coffee. We would sit at the kitchen table and try to carry on a conversation. At first we had a rather hard time understanding each other. I could not understand his accent and when he would smoke a cigar or simply hold one in his mouth unlit, it was even worse.

On the other hand I could tell he did not understand me at all but he was trying. I still smile now after so many years, remembering the expression on his face, not wanting to hurt my feelings. He would listen intently with eyes half closed nodding as if he knew what I was talking about. I feared that eventually he would get tired and bored and it would be the end of our early coffee breaks but somehow the next morning he would be there. After a couple of weeks I was getting accustomed to the American "slang" and I believe he was getting used to my French accent.

Cynthia his wife was now taking the breakfast issue on hand. She usually fixed bacon and eggs for everyone but I could not eat it. All I ever had was continental breakfast. So she started to bake cinnamon rolls. I was very happy with toast but she would not hear of it. She also saw that the cigar was put away from time to time.

I realized that both Jack and Cynthia had changed a few habits for my benefit. It made me appreciate the fact that they understood the tremendous changes I had to deal with everyday. I felt comfortable with them; I had found a family.

However I was also homesick. I kept in touch with my mother and family by mail but it was slow. The telephone was out of the question. It was operated by undewater cable and not only extremely expensive but also time consumming. One would have to place a call, then wait hours and the same waiting would be required at the other end of the line, regardless of the time difference.

Rosie was dating a very nice young man by the name of Kenneth. They had planned to attend a dance at Kiowa, Kansas, a little town not too far from Alva, Oklahoma, which was located on the Panhandle. They asked Merritt and I to join them and make a foursome. Rosie had been delegated by her parents to buy me something. I had brought a few souvenirs from France and assumed they all were trying to reciprocate.

She took me downtown to a very nice dress shop, picked out a black dress with a large white collar covered with loads of rhinestones and the next thing I was trying it on under the approving look of some customers and the owner of the shop. I protested but Rosie did not pay attention and I ended up with the dress.

Not knowing what kind of dance I was going to attend in Kiowa, I thought it would make everyone feel better if I wore the famous dress.

I asked at random what they thought, but only received a stare. So I approached Merritt point blank "What kind of dance is it?, What should I wear?" He thought I looked great in that dress but that was not the answer I expected. I finally dropped the subject thinking they knew their customs.

It turned out to be a big mistake. The Kiowa dance was supposed to be a western dance with all the trimmings: jeans, hats, boots and more. I felt like a fool. No one can guess the looks I received from men and women alike. Meanwhile, oblivious to my embarrassment, Rosie and Merritt were introducing me to a few people they knew. This was not their usual stomping ground. Rosie and Kenneth were both students at the Northwestern Oklahoma State University in Alva. Most of the crowd at the dance included students from Kiowa and the vicinity but all from Kansas. I could feel their competitiveness. From the looks I gathered there was no love lost between the schools.

I was sure once they learned I just arrived from France that I would not want to hear their comments. The "Olala!" followed by raucus laughter didn't help either. I was very hurt and wanted to get out of there.

I realized that my party was well aware of the tension but pretended to ignore it. No one wanted to get into a fight.

Driving back from Kiowa I didn't have much to say.

Merritt made the comment "Marie, you are very quiet, are you all right?"
"Yes, I am fine," I replied.

Not wanting to talk I closed my eyes the rest of the trip and listened to them talk about people, events and places I knew nothing about. If anything I felt worse; I really was an outsider.

The next morning at the kitchen table Jack seemed to have acquired a sixth sense.

"There are all kinds of people, some are ignorant, others are rude, don't pay attention", he said. "Don't get mad, get even, that's my motto." I remember Merritt having made the same comment on another occasion.

Rosie and Kenneth were planning to get married and they were having a big wedding. They wanted to make it a double wedding.

Merritt and I decided since I had no friends or family of my own in this country, it would be better to have a simple, quiet wedding. His folks thought it was a smart idea. So we went to New Mexico with close relatives and were married in Clayton.

After we were married I went to work for Old Surety Life, an insurance company in Alva. The owners were so nice and so were my co-workers. I enjoyed my new job and made many friends.

Merritt was a part-owner with his father of a hotel, restaurant and bar, called the Alva Hotel. The two managed the business, but Alva was a small college town and business was slow. It got progressively worse. It was difficult for the two of us just newlywed, to make enough money to support ourselves so we decided to move to Liberal, Kansas, a booming oil town, where Merritt was offered a good salary to work as a manager for a private club known as the High Plains Petroleum Club. I studied the opportunities available to me and decided that I would embrace a new career, the oil business.

At this point in my life I could not go back to school to learn all there was to know about the *oil industry* for many reasons. I had tremendous adjustments ahead of me, being from another country, actually another continent.

Everything Americans took for granted was new to me. I had always worked. I felt I had to continue and try to help Merritt earn our living. I had attended school, first in Italy then for the most part in France. All my records were still in Europe providing they had survived all of the chaos and bombardments of World War II.

I concluded the best thing to do was to find work with an oil company and learn as much as possible. I was aware that once a company hired me, they would first invest their time and money to train me since I was inexperienced. However, I also knew once I became good in a certain department they would be unwilling to transfer me to another one. Consequently I planned to work for various companies, making sure I would be able to learn a new phase of the oil business within each company. I promised myself that I would do the best in my power to make my employers proud of my work.

My first job was with Colorado Oil and Gas as a geological secretary for eight geologists. The previous secretary had left suddenly about a month earlier, for personal reasons, leaving the geologists stranded. They desperately needed someone to put some kind of order in their department which was overwhelmed with logs (a record of progress in drilling a well). The electric logs were usually about 5-inches wide and came in strips of various lengths. Some special envelopes had been created just for the purpose of filing them. The top part of the log indicated the well, location, company, all kinds of information. One needed to fold the log in an accordion shape with the information up front. The envelopes were to be labelled to match the logs.

I must say my first glance at the piled up work awaiting me was rather overwhelming. There were logs everywhere, draped over cabinets, desks, tables, stashed into boxes, taking up every space available. I may not have known about the oil business but I definitely knew about organization. I proceeded to get busy sorting, folding logs and labelling envelopes, then filing them according to the company's rules. My immediate goal was to get the office cleared and in working order. This was accomplished in record time.

Then my real experience began. One of the duties of a geological secretary was to spend most of the morning, writing, sending or receiving drilling reports on various wells that the company drilled or participated in the drilling. This was the hardest part of the job inasmuch as I was not familiar with terms and abbreviations. To add to my confusion most of the geologists were congregating in my office with one excuse or another and grinning. They loved my accent, so they said. It was very intimidating for me but after a while I managed to ignore them. I acquired a book called the *"ABC's of the Oil Business"* and it became my Bible (to this day I still have it).

I remained with Colorado Oil and Gas for almost three years, until they moved their offices to Denver, Colorado. I was offered a job in Denver but by then Merritt and I were settled in Liberal, Kansas, where we had purchased our first home and were raising our first child, Alan.

Merritt was very happy as the manager of the High Plains Petroleum Club. My mother had applied for a visa to come and see her first grandchild shortly after Alan was born. By that time I was staying home to take care of the baby. Finally mother announced she had received her visa and was on her way. I was thrilled; she would be with us to celebrate Alan's second birthday.

A couple of weeks before my mother was to sail from *Cannes, France*, the baby came down with a virus. After several trips to the emergency room his condition worsened. He was admitted to the hospital for all kinds of tests for meningitis and other illnesses. All we were told was that he had a virus.

Thus began a long non-ending nightmare for Merritt and I, an ordeal which was to last five days and five nights followed by grief and anguish the rest of our lives. Merritt's parents, sisters, everyone came to the hospital, taking turns. Except for brief trips home, we never left Alan's bedside. Merritt would check with the Club by phone from time to time. Liberal, Kansas was a small town and news traveled fast. The Governor of Kansas, having heard of Alan's illness, sent a plane to deliver a new serum. Learning this gave us renewed hope. However this was short-lived when we found out the hospital had been using the same serum without success.

On the 4th of December 1959, my husband and I had to face our first major tragedy. We had lost our son. No words can express our despair, sorrow and loss. I wired my family in France the terrible news. Not wanting to devastate my mother before her departure, she was told by my relatives that Alan was very ill, letting her believe there was little hope but not telling her the truth; the trip was going to be hard enough for her. We decided to drive to New York and meet her ship. When she saw us at the pier, no explanations were necessary; it was a terrible blow to her as well.

Back in Liberal, Kansas unable to deal with this enormous hardship, my husband asked for a job transfer. We chose to move to Casper, Wyoming to pick up the shattered pieces of our lives and start over once again. My mother was a tower of strength. I really don't know what we would have done without her.

The Casper Petroleum Club hired Merritt as their general manager. My mother and I remained in Liberal, Kansas in order to sell our house. Once this was accomplished we followed Merritt. I was expecting and we were anxious to get settled. In November our daughter was born; we named her *Cherie-Lynn*.

Once you lose a child you become paranoid and become extremely protective. The doctor suggested that I return to work and have my daughter lead a normal life. With my mother living with us, there was no problem.

I then went to work for Pan American Oil Company in the Purchasing and Expirations Department. I also attended school at night. Later, following my goal of learning all the phases of the oil industry, I acquired a part-time position with Mobil Oil for a six-month period and finally joined the firm of Stroock and Rogers Oil Co, where I worked in the Land Department. I became quite knowledgeable in the oil business.

In the meantime I participated in many of the functions held at the Club. I helped Merritt organize parties, balls, and various events. I also stood by his side, greeting the members and their spouses upon their arrival. I loved to dance and Merritt and I made a good team. My mother created many evening dresses for me. I have fond memories of that period in my life.

It was then that I was offered my first managerial position with John P. Ellbogen, an oil producer. Mr. Ellbogen, known as "Jack", was a sharp, shrewd, self-made man with a quick mind, who was extremely successful.

My position was Operations Manager and I was in charge of all co-workers. I oversaw all of the business and transactions that were made in the office and I had many responsibilities. I worked very hard. I truly loved my job, my co-workers and my boss. This was what I had worked so hard all my life to accomplish. I had achieved what I had set out to do.

After a while my mother decided to return to her own country. It was very difficult for her to live here; she did not speak English, she missed her sisters, brothers and her own life in general. She felt constricted, depending entirely on me for everything as she could not communicate with anyone. Therefore we made arrangements for her to return to France and Italy where she still had her home. Cherie was two years old by now. Mother had taught her Italian and of course we also spoke to Cherie in French. Merritt was concerned about Cherie getting confused with all the languages. Her pediatrician however put our minds to rest by asking " Do you know anyone that speaks Chinese? This would be the best time to learn". Needless to say we stopped at three languages. We taught her to answer in the same language in which she was spoken to.

We made the necessary reservations and decided I was going to take my mother to New York to board the ship for Cannes, France. First I was driving to Alva, Oklahoma to visit my father and mother- in- law. They were going to keep Cherie until I returned. However from Alva we had to go to Wichita by car to catch the train to New York. (My mother refused to fly). We remained in New York a couple of days as the train ride had been very tiring. Once I saw her safely onboard the ship, I caught the plane back to Wichita, where my sister-in-law was waiting to pick me up. Then after remaining in Alva a few more days, Cherie and I headed back to Casper. We already missed my mother a lot, however, it was her decision and her life.

Merritt was extremely busy managing the Petroleum Club which was fairly new. He worked split shifts and it was hard on all of us but we had to get adjusted. We made plans to go

My mother on her way home, Cheríe, Cynthia my mother in law in Alva, OK.

and see my mother as much as we could. As Cherie got older, I went every other year, sometimes just the two of us, Cherie and I and at other times with Merritt whenever he could get away.

Helping Merritt at the club.

At the club top.
Traveling in France left.
Palace de Versailles right.

**Cherie our daughter with Aunt
Zize in Juan-Les Pins.**

Obsession or Mystery

Since the death of my brother Nini, my mother and I spent many years trying to find out what had happened to him. We understood that many people were killed the same way during the war, where parents would wonder the real cause for their loved one's death.

In this instance it was different. To begin with Nini was not with a regular army. From the FFI group (French Resistance), he had ended up in extremely classified missions and was wearing an American Uniform.

We felt that the least the French Government could do was to give us a plausible answer when we ask for the circumstances of his death.

We had so many questions and we were given so few answers. We felt that something was being kept from us. This last mission that tragically had ended his life, could it have been avoided?

We were told that his mission had taken him in a different direction. Some of the answers indicated that he was first sent to Belgium, in the vicinity of Antwerpen. The Battle of the Bulge took place in this same area according to history and started December 16, 1944. My brother was killed December 11, 1944, near the German border, outside the town of Thann, located on the left of the city of Mulhouse, close to Switzerland.

He had been in charge of a Resistance group in the Saint Raphael Mountains for the FFI and was there to help with the landing of the Allies on the beach called *The Drammond*. He knew the dangers and had survived many close calls. Yet it seemed to us that he would not put his life and the lives of his closest friends and support group in jeopardy.

When my father was informed of our loss, he went to the town of Thann and received Nini's belongings. Later on he found a letter from Nini indicating that the Blue Ring was to be returned to me if anything should ever happen to him but there was no ring.

After being buried in *Thann*, his body was finally returned to *Menton* and received a full-honors funeral in the military cemetery. This was a couple of years later. He was awarded the "Croix de Guerre" and the "Legion d'Honneur".

My father who had entirely disappeared from our lives was nowhere to be found. However the last blow came when he deliberately failed to inform us of the transfer and burial arrangements of the victims made by the Government. This had been planned several weeks in advance. A special train was to leave the German border and bring the casualties across France all the way to the Italian border. This train was to make scheduled stops at the hometown of each victim, organized in such a way that a service was being performed on the train platform before the final rites in each town. *Menton*, close to the

Italian border was going to be the very last one.

Nini's hometown had been *Menton,* living with my father and grandparents. However neither my mother nor I were informed of the 'burial procession' as they called it. It was surprising because we had received the telegram upon his death. It was just accidentally and too late to go to *Menton,* that we heard of the special train requisitionned by the War Department in a news broadcast. I immediately called them to find out if my brother was part of this train's mission, and was told that Mr.Vella had decided to inform us personally. We managed to put together a memorial service in the town of *Marignane.* Needless to say my father's name was never to be mentioned again in our home.

Furthermore in order to clarify my doubts and thoughts and not being able to depend on my father after the terrible experience of the burial, I contacted the Deuxième Bureau directly (much like the CIA), who explained that his mission was related to a Nazi plot against the American Military Officials. Their briefing was deceptively vague. I then inquired about the blue ring Nini wore at all times. They had no idea what I was talking about.

Who had collected all of his personal belongings?

During his last visit, Nini had told me that he never took his ring off. He had taken precautions to protect it at all times and had added "It is too important, I cannot afford to loose it". However at the time I did not understand. He had mentioned that he was part of a very small group of four. They were called *"Eclaireurs de Reconnaisance"* which meant 'reconnaisance scouts'. they went everywhere together, and looked out for each other.

One of my aunts in *Marseille, France* told me that at one point she had a visitor claiming to be Nini's friend. He had gone to see her to offer his condolences many months later. He told her how the last mission had ended for the four of them. My aunt did not know about the ring; besides she was so upset at the time of the man's visit that she couldn't even remember his name. So someone was still alive, someone knew about Nini and perhaps the whereabouts of the Blue Ring. But who?

The absence of the ring was very perturbing to me. The mystery remained.

. . .

It was perhaps close to 20 years since my brother's death during World War II when the strangest encounter happened. I was on one of my frequent trips back to Europe where I would visit my mother and family. On that particular trip I had been asked to meet some of the people from the *American Embassy* in *Cannes* where the *"Festival International du Film"* was being held. As usual I was invited to some luncheons, banquets, screenings and events of all kinds, where I would be able to be an interpreter, if needed and socialize as well.

I had arrived very early because I wanted to do some shopping at *"La Rue d'Antibes"* where the most wonderful stores are still located. First, however, I wanted to go to an outdoor cafe on the *Promenade de la Croissette*, my favorite spot, where I could enjoy a *petit déjeuner* (continental breakfast) and watch the early morning crowd go by. The *Promenade* faced the beaches and was the most important avenue in *Cannes*. The famous Carlton Hotel was located on this promenade and this was where the special luncheon was taking place It was perfect with *"La Rue d'Antibes"* nearby. As I arrived, I chose an outdoor cafe, not too crowded, where I could have a wonderful view of the sea and let my thoughts carry me back to the earlier years of my life.

I sat at a little table and ordered a brioche (French pastry) and a cup of café-au-lait. Only two other tables were occupied. As I casually looked around a flash of light attracted my attention. A gentleman was seated at an angle across from me. The morning sunlight was catching the gem on the ring he wore as he turned the pages of the morning paper that he was reading. I spent some time enjoying the entire ambiance surrounding me, watching the people on the promenade and on the beaches. Looking out at the Mediterranean Sea, the water was such a deep blue, along with the never ending rows of palm trees, and the vast variety of flower beds that bordered the beach front. I felt like I was in heaven and its beauty never ceased to amaze me. As it always did, my thoughts wandered back to my years when I lived on the *French Riviera* and with Nini in *Menton*.

The waiter disrupted my concentration by asking me if everything was fine and if I wished for anything else. I thanked him and resumed my perusing of the area. Again that flash! This time however, I started to look seriously at the cause of this light. A picture began to appear in my mind. As I began to focus on it more deeply with the reflecting sun, I realized that the image in my mind became that of my family's crest. "This is really getting to be an obsession with you" I told myself. Still I realized I could not let it go. I debated how I could take a closer look before the gentleman decided to leave.

Aware of my intense stare, he smiled, nodded and then resumed reading. I was extremely embarrassed having been caught staring, yet I had to have a second look at his ring. Boldly, I approached the gentleman at his table. *"Monsieur,"* I began, *"excusez-moi, je m'appelle Marie-Jeanne Darr. Je suis des Etats Unis, Française de naissance. Je voudrais simplement voir votre bague de prés. Elle ressemble enormément à celle de ma famille"*. (Translated: " Sir, please excuse me. My name is Marie-Jeanne Darr. I am from the United States, yet a native of France. I would like to take a close look at your ring. It resembles a ring of my family.")

He rose, then introduced himself. His name was Réne Montigne and he invited me to join him for a cup of coffee at his table. The name sounded vaguely familiar. Where had I heard it? There was a minute or two of uneasiness. I felt that the man was taken aback by my aggressiveness, yet curious about my intense interest. At the mention of my name "Marie-Jeanne", I had seen a flicker of interest which faded the minute I added my last name "Darr".

Sitting there, I could not take my eyes away from the ring he wore, while he continued to observe me trying to figure out what my intentions were. He made a lot of small talk asking me questions such as: What part of America I was from? What was I doing in France? I told him that I was on vacation visiting family, helping with the Cannes Film Festival, etc. Finally, he asked me, "Do you have a brother?" I told him, "My brother was killed during the war and my interest in the ring was because of him. He was supposed to be wearing one just like this one," and I pointed to the ring this gentleman was wearing on his finger. Suddenly, with a sudden gist of inspiration, I heard myself asking him, "Would it be possible for me to try your ring on?" He complied , took the ring off his finger and gave it to me.

The minute I held the ring and began to place it on my finger, I knew this was Nini's blue ring. As I was wearing the ring, I remembered there was a way to open it; it was difficult to find, I recalled. So I took the ring off and started to put pressure points on different areas. Suddenly as I had expected the ring opened up, revealing a secret compartment. The surprise on the man's face was truly genuine. He actually looked stunned. I was also overwhelmed.

In the cavity of the ring, there was a minute piece of paper of some kind and perhaps some lint. Upon seeing this, we just looked at each other. When he recovered his composure, he asked me to close the ring and reopen it. I told him I could close it I thought but I did not know for sure how to reopen it. I handed the ring back to him We spent some time trying to reopen it and finally succeeded. Then he exclaimed, "I have been wearing this ring for years on and off and I never knew of the existence of this compartment!"

I proceeded to recount the story my grandfather used to tell us about the ring, explaining about our family ancestors. As we continued talking, it turned out that Nini had been a friend of this gentleman, René, but they had never discussed the matter of their backgrounds. All that René knew was that the ring was very special to Nini and he had made him promise that if something should ever happen to him, he would see that the ring was returned to me alone. Nini didn't want anyone else in the Vella family to have it.

He went on to recount the years that he and Nini were friends. They played music together, went to the same schools, studied pretty much the same subjects and received their diplomas at the same time. When things got tough they had decided that "France" needed them and they joined the "Maquis". When Nini was sent on secret missions, René was always part of the team, as well as their two other friends, Louis and Serge. Finally, Nini was taken into the American Army, at least this is what we thought as he wore an American Uniform; shorthly thereafter René followed suit. When Nini had been assigned to certain missions, René had volunteered to go with him as a contact. Later the other two, Serge and Louis followed as backup men. He did not know what the last mission had been about, but according to all the actions and precautionary measures taken at the time, it must have been very serious and dangerous. All René knew was that this mission entailed the collecting or delivering of important information concerning a German plot to eliminate certain American leaders. All three had been a part of the team with Nini. René had been wounded and eventually recovered. Nini, Louis and Serge had not been so lucky.

After the war René had tried to find me. First he had tried to find my father without success, then he contacted anyone of the Vella family, however, it seems there was a wall of silence or perhaps they did not know.

As I mentioned before, I had no contact at all with any of my father's relatives. As far as I know no one knew that I had married and gone to America. So René just kept the ring all of this time, not knowing what else he should do.

I mentioned to him that after my brother's death my father had entirely fallen apart and had disappeared. A long silence followed.

As I took a sip of my coffee I recalled the circumstances of the last time I saw my father.

Not caring to tell anyone where he had gone, he just vanished. I did not hear from my father for seventeen years. Then one year I was in Italy with Chérie, my daughter, who was three years old at that time. In my family's large dining room on the ground floor of our home in Perinaldo we were having coffee and pastries and were just talking with relatives and friends when the door bell rang. I went to open the door and I just stood there staring into my father's face. He had changed so much that I didn't even recognize him at first. He walked in, greeted everyone, and announced that he had come to meet his granddaughter. I was a little stunned by this. Addressing me from the middle of the room my father said that he had kept track of me throughout the years and that he knew about the loss of my son and how sorry he was. He then told everyone that he was now driving for the Reverend's mother who was in charge of a Catholic Organization that was located in *Menton*. He had brought her to the church and decided to stop by. Everyone was frozen in their chairs and my mother just stared at him, tight-lipped, too angry to speak. (My mother had never forgiven my father for his past actions and behavior. Nini's burial circumstances were the last thing she would forgive I never had forgiven my father for this either.)

Finally my Aunt Honorine told my daughter, "Chérie, go and say hello to your grandfather. I remember watching my daughter innocently walk toward my father and boldly say, *"Bonjour, Pépé!"* It was his turn to be speechless. Someone offered refreshments while I was still rooted to the front door. Still angry at my father, I had so many questions to ask that I didn't even know where to start Before I could begin to speak, my father, declining refreshments, was on his way out as if he were running away from something. He never even touched my daughter.

René and I remained at the café for a long time thinking back and trying to understand each person's side of the story.

Finally René looking at the contents of the ring said, "This is not just paper inside, it is microfilm and I don't want to take it out myself; it looks like it is all deteriorated and I don't want to risk ruining it even more. It's best that I take this ring to the authorities and have them do it. I will have to contact them either in St. Raphael or Marseille."

"I could come to St. Raphaël myself," I offered. "How long are you going to be staying?" he asked. "Another two weeks," I replied. "Then I will meet you here, probably next week. I have to come back to see a client. In the meantime I am going to get in touch with someone both Nini and I knew who used to be with the *Deuxieme Bureau*... how may I reach you?" He seemed preoccupied. We exchanged telephone numbers and went our separate ways.

I returned to my Aunt Zize's home in Juan-les-Pins where I was staying and who had been keeping *Cherie* and told her of the encounter and the discovery of the ring. Her skeptical look confirmed my own thoughts, I should probably forget about it.

Nevertheless, three days later the phone rang and it was René. He was going to meet me the following day in Cannes; we decided on the same place as before, only later in the afternoon after his appointment with his client. True to his word, René arrived with the blue ring minus the microfilm.

He handed me the ring and said: "The authorities did not know if the microfilm could be of any use because so much time had lapsed and it was in bad shape." And he added, "Even if they could tell, we will never know."

Neither of us wanted to leave, I wanted to hear everything he could tell me about Nini and he was very interested about my accomplishments. It seemed that Nini had known the role I had played in a small way for the *Resistance* and was proud of me.

He told me I should be very proud of my brother, he was truly a hero.

Always optomestic, cheerful under all circumstances, he had high standards and was respected by friends and feared by enemies. He had taken big risks, many times and had helped his fellow men in tough circumstances. Before they left for the last mission Nini had taken René aside and asked him if he would wear the ring. He told him it had something to do with being a target. Either he carried something important or someone had a description of him, René did not know, but Nini definitely knew.

"If anything should happen to me get a hold of my sister and give her the ring, she'll know what to do." Again he repeated "Do not give it to any of the Vella."

Later on they were caught in an ambush and all four were shot down. René was the only sur-

Nini, Serge and Louis.

vivor and for a long time they did not know if he was going to survive his wounds. He remained in the hospital for months.

Currently he was in Cannes on business. He did not say much about his family, if any, and I did not ask. I was still under the shock of what he had told me about the other two friends Serge and Louis being shot down at the same time. I recalled a picture of three of them playing music that my brother had sent to me. I would have to check it out. René must have been in the picture or else he was the photographer.

We finally said good-bye and agreed to keep in touch. When he left, I could sense he was a bit upset. I had mixed feelings myself. I felt a little guilty as I walked away, wearing the ring after so many years, but then, as I took a long look at it, I knew this was Nini's will.

. . .

At first, I felt exhilarated! I had the ring back and this was absolutely incredible! Now, I thought to myself, my life would be back on track. I always felt like something was missing and now with the ring this empty, hollow feeling that I had, would disappear. My search for my brother's blue ring was now over. I really felt complete. As I went to sleep that night, my last thoughts were of the Blue Ring and they were the first when I awoke the next morning.

Strangely enough, however, this feeling of elation was very short lived. It brought back so many memories. Having the ring back I began to take an inventory of my life. As I looked back I told myself that I was "Blue Blood"; this however did not mean a thing in America even if it still did in Europe; I had reached my goals on my own merit in this country.

I had never told anyone about my ancestors or my heritage. I thought, what's the use? I did write it down for my children's sake and I had mentioned it briefly to my husband, but that was the extent of it.

I will always love my native country, France, but America was very much a part of me now. America had opened her arms to me and had given me a better life than I had living in Europe. I had respect, friends, and love. When I first arrived in this country I felt accepted, welcomed, even admired and this feeling is still with me today.

Recovering the Blue Ring was like reaching out to Nini, hearing him speak of values, giving me advice, sharing our hopes, and most of all knowing he was there for me- my big brother, but those days were over.

While I held the Blue Ring and was reminiscing, an indescribable feeling of emptiness filled me. Did I worship the memory of this ring and what it represented or was it the part the ring had played in my brother's life? I was confused, unhappy. Had I put too much emphasis into finding this ring, using this as an excuse to acknowledge the real problem; the loss of Nini? This ring was not mine. This ring was and always will be Nini's. It held secrets of all of his missions. Just the fact that he gave it to René before his fatal mission told me that he knew that he was not going to come back. He must have known that this was where it would end for him. This ring did not belong in America. So I decided to leave it in France. But where?

I had to go to *Menton* to visit Nini's grave, maybe I would think of something. My aunt mentioned that my father used to be well known at the City Hall, I could probably trace some of my father's contacts there.

Once in *Menton* and after an extended research, I found that my father had kept a safe deposit box in a small bank in the past. At the time the banking business was not what it is now. During the war, normally people kept their money and valuables at home in a hidden place. My father was constantly on the move so perhaps he found it convenient. I was curious to know what the box contained. The Bank Official suggested that if I wanted to open a box I probably could use that one and by doing so it would give me a chance to see what was inside after I had proven my identity. It took several days for them to complete all of the paper work and formalities so that I could have access to this box.

When we opened the box nothing of importance was found. Simply some papers issued to Jean Vella, my grandfather. I decided that this would be the most appropriate place for the blue ring. It seemed perfect! The bank could not find a card that would give anyone else authorization to enter the box beside my late father. Since I was on my way back to the States, I paid for an additional year rental and directed them to mail me all future correspondence to Casper, Wyoming.

Once back home I explained to Merritt what had happened, the meeting with René, the finding of the ring and the fact that I had decided to leave it

Nini in an American uniform.

there in my father's old safety box. He didn't see anything wrong with it, he respected my feelings and had not realized how important all that had been to me .

Back in the States, I resumed my busy life. It was a comforting thought to know that the ring was now in a vault in Menton; in my mind it was like a burial place for it. Something was still nagging at me but I could not exactly pinpoint it.

Then I received a letter from René. He had made some inquiries and had discovered that my brother was not killed instantly; he had been severely injuried and was taken to a temporary medical facility where he later died. René added that perhaps whatever the mission was that he had been entrusted with may have been carried out. This was just an assumption on his part of course, but it did lift my heart. If this mission was so important to my brother that he was willing to risk his life for it, I prayed that somehow it had been completed.

How incredible that my brother would be the one to prevent some major disaster to occur while wearing, with much pride, the American Uniform. He fought like a million others and helped defeat an enemy and hasten the end of a terrible war, not only for France, but for all Nations, for Humanity and Freedom.

The Blue Ring

The Blue Ring

The Blue Ring